THE CHARLTON STANDARD CATALOGUE OF

ROYAL DOULTON BESWICK STORYBOOK FIGURINES

SIXTH EDITION

BY
JEAN DALE

INTRODUCTION
BY
LOUISE IRVINE

W. K. CROSS
PUBLISHER

The Charlton Press
TORONTO, ONTARIO ◆ PALM HARBOR, FLORIDA

The Charlton Press

Editorial Office
2040 Yonge Street, Suite 208, Toronto, Canada M4S 1Z9
Telephone (416) 488-1418 Fax: (416) 488-4656
Telephone (800) 442-6042 Fax: (800) 442-1542
www.charltonpress.com e-mail: chpress@charltonpress.com

EDITORIAL

Editor	Jean Dale
Graphic Technician	Davina Rowan
Photography	Marilyn and Peter Sweet

ACKNOWLEDGEMENTS

The Charlton Press wishes to thank those who have helped with the sixth edition of *The Charlton Standard Catalogue of Royal Doulton Beswick Storybook Figurines*.

Special Thanks

The publisher would like to thank Louise Irvine for writing the introduction to this edition. Louise is an independent writer and lecturer on Royal Doulton's history and products and is not connected with the pricing in this price guide.

We would also like to thank Carolyn Baker for all the work on the Beatrix Potter series, both for this edition and previous editions.

Our thanks also go to the staff of Royal Doulton, who have helped with additional technical information, especially Valerie Baynton, Janet Drift, Ian Howe, Julie McKeown, Kevin Moyer and Maria Murtagh.

Contributors to the Sixth Edition

The publisher would also like to thank the following individuals and companies who graciously supplied photographs or information or allowed us access to their collections for photographic purposes: **Chris Back**, Backstamp Collectables, Cambridgeshire, England; **George and Nora Bagnall**, Precious Memories, Charlottetown, P.E.I.; **John and Diana Callow**, England; **Frank Corley**, Alexandria, VA; **William T. Cross**, William Cross Antiques and Collectibles, Burnaby, B.C.; **Louise Fundenberg**, Newport Beach, California; **William Haight**, Sarnia, Ontario; **Gordon Hopper**, England; **Suzanne Morgan**, Evesham, England; **Roland Matthews,** Surrey, England; **Andrew Reid**, By Dollar, Scotland; **Carol Scott**, Lakefield Marketing Limited, Cumbria, England; **Leah Selig**, Merrylands, Australia; **Marilyn and Peter Sweet**, Bolton, England; **Gene Truitt**, Tru-Find Collectibles, Virginia; **Stan Worrey**, Colonial House, Berea, Ohio.

A SPECIAL NOTE TO COLLECTORS

We welcome and appreciate any comments or suggestions in regard to *The Charlton Standard Catalogue of Royal Doulton Beswick Storybook Figurines*. If any errors or omissions come to your attention, please write to us, or if you would like to participate in pricing or supply previously unavailable data or information, please contact Jean Dale at (416) 488-1418, or e-mail us at chpress@charltonpress.com.

DISCLAIMER

Canadian Cataloguing In Publication Data

The National Library of Canada has catalogued this publication as follows:

Charlton standard catalogue of Royal Doulton Beswick storybook figurines (1995)
  The Charlton standard catalogue of Royal Doulton Beswick storybook figurines

Annual.
3rd ed.-
Vols. for 1996- by Jean Dale.
ISSN 1198-1652
ISBN 0-88968-248-8 (6th ed.)

1. Beswick (Firm) - Themes, motives - Catalogs. 2. Royal Doulton figurines - Catalogs. 3. Porcelain animals - England - Catalogs. 4. Porcelain animals - Prices - Catalogs. 5. Royal Doulton figurines - Prices - Catalogs. I. Dale, Jean, II. Charlton International Inc. III. Title. IV. Title: Royal Doulton Beswick storybook figurines.

NK4660.C467	738.8'2	C99-390043-7

**Printed in Canada
in the Province of Manitoba**

HOW TO USE THIS PRICE GUIDE

THE PURPOSE

The sixth edition of this price guide covers the complete range of children's figures issued by Royal Doulton and Beswick with the exception of the Bunnykins figurines which are included in *The Charlton Standard Catalogue of Royal Doulton Bunnykins*, First Edition. In the process we have taken liberties with the name of this catalogue, for all figures listed are certainly not derived from storybook characters. However, the great majority are, and thus we have carried the name forward.

As with the other catalogues in Charlton's Royal Doulton reference and pricing library, this publication has been designed to serve two specific purposes. First, to furnish the collector with accurate and detailed listings that provide the essential information needed to build a rewarding collection. Second, to provide collectors and dealers with current market prices for Royal Doulton and Beswick storybook figures.

STYLES AND VERSIONS

STYLES: A change in style occurs when a major element of the design is altered or modified as a result of a deliberate mould change. An example of this is *The Duchess With Flowers* (style one) and *The Duchess With a Pie* (style two).

VERSIONS: Versions are modifications in a minor style element, such as the long ears becoming short ears on *Mr. Benjamin Bunny*.

VARIATIONS: A change in colour is a variation; for example, *Mr. Jeremy Fisher*'s change in colourways from spotted to striped leggings.

THE LISTINGS

The Beatrix Potter figures are arranged alphabetically. At the beginning of the Beatrix Potter listings are five pages graphically outlining backstamp variations. Backstamps are illustrated for eleven major varieties covering over fifty years of production. In the Beatrix Potter pricing charts, the reader will see Beswick and Doulton model numbers, backstamp numbers and market prices.

The Brambly Hedge figures are listed by their DBH numbers. There are no backstamp variations known.

The Snowman series is listed in numerical order by the DS numbers. There are no backstamp variations.

All of the above listings include the modeller, where known, the name of the animal figure, designer, height, colour, date of issue, varieties and series.

A WORD ON PRICING

The purpose of this catalogue is to give readers the most accurate, up-to-date retail prices for Royal Doulton and Beswick figurines in the United States, Canada, the United Kingdom and Australia.

To accomplish this, The Charlton Press continues to access an international pricing panel of experts who submit prices based on both dealer and collector retail-price activity, as well as current auction results in the U.S.A., Canada, and the U.K. These market prices are carefully averaged to reflect accurate valuations for figures in each of these markets.

The prices published herein are for figurines in mint condition. Collectors are cautioned that a repaired or restored piece may be worth as little as 25 percent of the value of the same figure in mint condition.

Current figurines are priced according to the manufacturer's suggested retail price in each of the market regions. Please be aware that price or promotional sales discounting is always possible and can result in lower prices than those listed.

One exception, however, occurs in the case of current figurines or recent limited editions issued in only one of the three markets. Since such items were priced by Doulton only in the country in which they were to be sold, prices for the other markets are not shown.

A further word on pricing. As mentioned previously, this is a catalogue giving prices for figurines in the currency of a particular market (U.S. dollars for the American market and sterling for the U.K. market). The bulk of the prices given herein are not determined by currency exchange calculations, but by actual market activity in the market concerned.

In some cases the number of models produced is so small that market activity does not exist and there is very little activity on which to base a price. An example of this is the *Mr. Toadflax* (tail in front) from Brambly Hedge. The price in this instance is purely between the buyer and the seller. We have therefore listed the last known auction price for this model. If this model was to be offered for sale at a future date the price may be higher or lower than the auction price listed depending on the demand for the model at that time.

When prices are italicized in the pricing tables, for example, for *Duchess*, this signifies that the price is only an indication. The prices are too volatile to establish a solid market price. Once again, the final price determination must be made between buyer and seller.

THE INTERNET AND PRICING

The Internet is changing the way business is done in the collectable marketplace. Linking millions of collectors around the world through chat rooms, antique and collector malls, Internet auctions and producer websites, e-commerce has become big business.

Some of the effects caused by the Internet and e-commerce on the collectables business are as follows:

1. Collectors deal directly with other collectors, changing the dynamics of the traditional customer/dealer relationship.

2. Information concerning new issues, finds and varieties is readily available, twenty-four hours a day. Collectors' wants are made known instantly to a wide spectrum of dealers and collectors.

3. Prices:
   (a) Price differentials will disappear between global market areas as collectors and delivery services team up to stretch the purchasing power of the collectable dollar/pound.
   (b) Prices of common to scarce items will adjust downward to compensate for the temporary expansion of merchandise supply. Conversely, prices of rare and extremely rare items will increase, a result of their increased exposure to demand.
   (c) After a time even the prices of the common items will rise due to the growing worldwide demand for collectables.

4. Internet auction sites listing millions of items for sale on a daily basis continue to grow as more and more collectors discover the viability of using this method to buy and sell merchandise.

5. Traditional marketing strategies (retail stores, direct mail retailers, collectable shows and fairs, and collectable magazines and papers) face increased pressure in a more competitive environment.

YEAR CYPHERS

Figurines from the 101 Dalmatians, Snow White and the Seven Dwarfs and the Winnie the Pooh series now carry the year cypher.

The cypher for 1998 was an umbrella, 1999 was the Top Hat as worn by Sire Henry Doulton, and the cypher for 2000 is a fob watch.

A folded umbrella
the 1998 cypher

The Top Hat as worn by
Sir Henry Doulton
the 1999 cypher

A fob watch containing
the logo Millennium 2000

CONTENTS

Benjamin, The Beswick Bear
Compton & Woodhouse

INTRODUCTION
By Louise Irvine

THE HISTORY OF STORYBOOK CHARACTERS FROM THE ROYAL DOULTON, JOHN BESWICK AND ROYAL ALBERT STUDIOS

For over a century, the Royal Doulton Studios have entertained us with storybook characters, particularly animals endowed with human personalities. In Victorian times, a group of frogs enacting a well-known fable raised a smile in much the same way as the antics of the BRAMBLY HEDGE™ mice amuse us today. The tales of BEATRIX POTTER™, with lots of different animals acting and conversing as if they were human, are as popular now as when they were first written in the early 1900s. Obviously the idea of a creature simultaneously human and animal is deep rooted in our literary culture, and it is interesting to trace when it first became apparent in the Doulton world.

A Tinworth mouse group

The Doulton factory was founded in London in 1815, but for the first 50 years production was confined to practical pottery. In the late 1860s, Sir Henry Doulton established an art studio, employing students from the Lambeth School of Art to decorate vases, jugs and plaques in fashionable Victorian styles. Some artists specialised in figurative sculpture, notably George Tinworth, who was the first to seek inspiration from well-known stories. The Bible provided him with most of his subject matter, but he also enjoyed reading the fables of Aesop and La Fontaine. These moralistic tales feature foxes, mice, lions and other creatures exemplifying human traits, and they fascinated the Victorians, particularly after the publication of Darwin's theory of evolution. Tinworth modelled several fables groups in the 1880s, including *The Fox and the Ape, The Cat and the Cheese* and *The Ox and the Frogs.* Later he produced mice and frog subjects, based on his own observations of human nature, which reflect his perceptive sense of humour.

The potential for dressed-up animals to disguise a deeper message soon led to their widespread use in children's literature, notably *Alice's Adventures in Wonderland* and Lear's nonsense poems. In 1908, Kenneth Grahame wrote *The Wind in the Willows* to comment on the behaviour of the English aristocracy, but the exciting adventures of Mr. Toad subtly conceal the author's critical stance. The dapper toad in his pinstripes and tails was modelled shortly afterwards by Lambeth artist Francis Pope, and a companion piece shows Mr. Toad disguised as a washerwoman in order to escape from prison.

Mr. Toad disguised as a washerwoman

Figures like these probably encouraged Beatrix Potter to approach the Lambeth studio in 1908 with a view to having her own animal characters immortalised in ceramic. Miss Potter published several illustrated stories about her favourite animals after the success of *The Tale of Peter Rabbit*™ in 1902, and some characters had already appeared as cuddly toys and decorative motifs on clothes, etc. Unfortunately an earlier contract with a German china firm made any arrangement with Doulton impossible, but she tried on a later occasion to have figures made of her characters at Grimwade's factory in Stoke-on-Trent. They suggested that Doulton's other factory in Burslem would be the best place to have the figures decorated, but again plans fell through. It was not until after Miss Potter's death that her dream was realised when the John Beswick factory in Longton began making little figures inspired by her books.

The John Beswick factory was founded in 1894 to produce ornamental jugs, vases and other decorative fancies. By the 1940s the Beswick artists had established a reputation for quality animal modelling, particularly portraits of famous horses by Arthur Gredington. In 1947, Gredington demonstrated his versatility when he modelled *Jemima Puddleduck* at the suggestion of Lucy Beswick, the wife of the managing director. She had been inspired by a visit to Beatrix Potter's Lake District home, where many of the tales are set. The success of this first study led to an initial collection of ten Beatrix Potter characters, including *Peter Rabbit*, *Benjamin Bunny* and *Mrs. Tiggy-Winkle*.

A group of Beatrix Potter books with the figures beside

Launched in 1948, the new Beatrix Potter figures were welcomed with enthusiasm, and it was not long before Gredington was at work on another collection of character animals, this time from a British animated film. The *Lion* cartoon by David Hand was released in 1948, and *Zimmy Lion* became a new star for the Rank Film Organisation. Sequel cartoons introduced *Ginger Nutt*, *Hazel Nutt*, *Dinkum Platypus*, *Loopy Hare*, *Oscar Ostrich*, *Dusty Mole* and *Felia Cat*, all of which were modelled in 1949 as the *DAVID HAND'S ANIMALAND*™ series. David Hand had formerly worked for the Walt Disney studios, directing Mickey Mouse shorts, as well as the major films *Snow White* and *Bambi*, and it was not long

before these cartoons also inspired a collection of Beswick figures. Arthur Gredington modelled the little figures of *Snow White and the Seven Dwarfs* whilst Jan Granoska, a trainee modeller, was given the task of portraying Mickey Mouse and friends, plus some characters from *Pinocchio* and *Peter Pan*. Although Miss Granoska was only at the Beswick studio for three years, she was responsible for some of their most desirable figures.

Music (of sorts!) is being played by the BEDTIME CHORUS™, a group of enthusiastic children accompanied by a singing cat and dog. These were amongst the first character figures to be modelled by Albert Hallam, who gradually took over responsibility for this area in the 1960s. As head mouldmaker, Hallam had made many of the production moulds for Gredington designs, so he was already familiar with the subject matter. He continued the *Beatrix Potter* collection, adding characters such as *Old Mr. Brown* and *Cecily Parsley*, and in 1968 he launched a new Disney series based on their newest cartoon hit, *Winnie the Pooh and the Blustery Day*.

The late 1960s was a time of transition for the company as Ewart Beswick was ready to retire but he had no heir for his successful business. Fortunately the Royal Doulton group was in the midst of an expansion programme and they acquired the Beswick factory in 1969. They soon benefited from Beswick's expertise in the field of character animals.

When Albert Hallam retired in 1975, Graham Tongue became the head modeller at the Beswick Studio under Harry Sales, the newly appointed design manager. Harry Sales was primarily a graphic artist and he dreamed up many new ideas for the Beatrix Potter range, which Graham Tongue and others modelled during the 1980s. This was becoming increasingly difficult as the most popular characters had already been modelled. Favourites, such as *Peter Rabbit* and *Jemima Puddleduck*, were introduced in new poses, and he came up with the idea of double figures, for example *Mr Benjamin Bunny and Peter Rabbit* and *Tabitha Twitchet and Miss Moppet*.

As well as developing the established figure collections, Harry Sales delved into lots of other children's books for inspiration. He re-interpreted the timeless characters from classic tales such as *Alice's Adventures in Wonderland* and *The Wind in the Willows*, and he worked from contemporary picture books, notably Joan Walsh Anglund's *A Friend is Someone Who Likes You* and Norman Thelwell's *Angels on Horseback*. Whenever possible, Harry liaised closely with the originators of the characters he portrayed. He spent many happy hours of research at Thelwell's studio, studying his cartoons of shaggy ponies with comical riders, and he also worked with Alfred Bestall, the illustrator of the Rupert Bear adventures in the *Daily Express* newspaper before embarking on this series in 1980.

With their outstanding reputation for developing character animals, it is not surprising that Royal Doulton artists were invited to work on the publishing sensation of the 1980s, the Brambly Hedge stories by Jill Barklem.

Within three years of their launch the *Spring, Summer, Autumn* and *Winter* stories had been reprinted 11 times, translated into ten languages, and had sold in excess of a million copies. Readers young and old were captivated by the enchanting world of the Brambly Hedge mice, as indeed was Harry Sales, whose job it was to recreate the characters in the ceramic medium. In his own words, "The first time I read the books and studied the illustrations I felt that I was experiencing something quite unique. Over a period of many years designing for the pottery industry one develops an awareness, a feeling for that something special. Brambly Hedge had this."

Ideas flowed quickly and eight leading characters were chosen from the seasonal stories for the initial collection, which was launched in 1983. Such was the response that they were soon joined by six more subjects, making a total of 14 by 1986, when Harry left the company. Graham Tongue succeeded him as design manager and continued to add new Brambly Hedge figures from the original stories. Miss Barklem's later titles, *The Secret Staircase, The High Hills* and *The Sea Story*, provided inspiration for some of his figures; for example, *Mr and Mrs Saltapple* who supply the Brambly Hedge community with salt in *The Sea Story*.

Encouraged by the amazing success of the Brambly Hedge collection, Royal Doulton's marketing executives were soon considering other new storybook characters. Like millions of TV viewers, they were spellbound by the magical film, *The Snowman*, which was first screened in 1982. Based on the illustrated book of the same name by Raymond Briggs, the animated film about a snowman who comes to life has become traditional Christmas entertainment in many parts of the world. The absence of words gives the tale a haunting quality, and there is hardly a dry eye in the house when the little boy, James, awakes to find his Snowman friend has melted away after an exciting night exploring each other's worlds. Fortunately the SNOWMAN™ lives on in more durable form in the Royal Doulton collection. Again Harry Sales was given the challenge of transforming this amorphous character into ceramic, whilst remaining faithful to Briggs' original soft crayon drawings. He succeeded in this difficult task by adding additional curves to the contours of the figures which gives them a life-like appearance. The first four figures were ready and approved by Raymond Briggs in 1985, and the collection grew steadily until 1990, latterly under the direction of Graham Tongue.

The 1990s saw Graham Tongue and his team of artists develop the Beatrix Potter collection for the 100th birthday of *Peter Rabbit* and, in 1994, the centenary of the Beswick factory was marked with the launch of the *Pig Promenade*, featuring a special commemorative backstamp.

This series is just one of three new collections of novelty figures, and it is refreshing to see this traditional type of Beswick ware being revitalised by a new generation of artists. Amanda Hughes-Lubeck and Warren Platt created the LITTLE LOVABLES™, a series of cute clowns with special messages, such as "Good Luck" and "Congratulations," and they also worked with Martyn Alcock on the collection of ENGLISH COUNTRY FOLK™, which has been very well received.

The collecting of Beatrix Potter and Brambly Hedge figures has reached epidemic proportions in recent years, and there is now a growing awareness of the desirability of all their storybook cousins, hence the need for this much expanded price guide.

COLLECTING BEATRIX POTTER FIGURES

A number of factors have combined recently to make Beatrix Potter figures the "hottest" collectables of the day. The 100th birthday of *Peter Rabbit* was celebrated amidst a storm of publicity in 1993, and the centenary of the John Beswick factory in 1994 focused a lot of collector attention on its products. 1997 saw more celebrations as Beatrix Potter figures had been in continuous production at Beswick for fifty years.

The market has been stimulated by regular withdrawals from the range and prices are rocketing for the early discontinued figures. Most collectors will need a bank loan to purchase *Duchess with Flowers*, the first Beatrix Potter figure to be retired, if indeed they are lucky enough to find one for sale.

Ever since the Beswick factory launched their Beatrix Potter collection in 1948, most of the figures have been bought as gifts for children. However, many young fans have grown up to find they have some valuable figures, with early modelling and backstamp variations, and they have begun collecting in earnest to fill the gaps and find the rarities. Figures marked with a Beswick backstamp are most in demand, as this trademark was replaced with the Royal Albert backstamp in 1989. The Royal Albert factory, another famous name in the Doulton group, produces all the Beatrix Potter tableware, and the change of backstamps was made for distribution reasons. The most desirable Beswick marks are the gold varieties, which predate 1972, and these are often found on early modelling or colour variations, which also attract a premium price, for example *Mrs Rabbit* with her umbrella sticking out and *Mr Benjamin Bunny* with his pipe protruding.

As well as seeking out discontinued figures and rare variations, it is advisable to keep up to date with new models as they are introduced. A complete Beatrix Potter figure collection will encompass more than 100 of the standard-size models, around three inches tall, and thirteen large models, which are about twice the size. *Peter Rabbit*, the first of these large size models, was launched in 1993 with a special commemorative backstamp from the John Beswick studio, and it changed in 1994 to a Royal Albert mark. The Royal Albert mark was used on most Beatrix Potter figures between 1989 and 1998 when new John Beswick backstamps were introduced.

If owning all the Beatrix Potter figures is beyond the realms of possibility, whether for financial or display limitations, then why not focus on particular types of animals or characters from your favourite tales. There are twenty mice figures to find, a dozen cat characters and more than twenty rabbits, half of which feature *Peter Rabbit*. There are also discontinued character jugs, relief modelled plaques and a ceramic display stand to look out for, so happy hunting.

COLLECTING BRAMBLY HEDGE FIGURES

Since their introduction in 1983, the Brambly Hedge mice have overrun households in many parts of the world. They are scurrying about the shelves as Royal Doulton figures and even climbing up the walls on decorative plates. Far from being undesirable, these particular mice are considered indispensable members of the family. Children frequently receive them as gifts from doting grandparents, but adults have also been seduced by the cosy, timeless mouse world which Jill Barklem has created. The mood of rustic nostalgia has all been painstakingly researched. The interiors of the field mice homes are of the sort common in English farmhouses at the end of the 19th century, and the food served is genuine country fare, based on old recipes and tested in Jill Barklem's kitchen. The Brambly Hedge residents were all expertly drawn with the aid of her two mouse models, a keen understanding of zoology and a knowledge of historical costume.

The same attention to detail went into the Royal Doulton figures designed by Harry Sales. As he explains, "One important feature in the concept was that I chose poses which, when the figures are together, appear to be reacting to one another. I can imagine the fun children and the young at heart will have arranging the figures in conversational situations." Essentially this sums up the collectability of the Brambly Hedge mice, and as there are only 25 figures in the first series, they can all be displayed effectively together on one shelf. There are, however, a couple of unusual modelling variations to look out for as *Mr Toadflax's* tail was altered shortly after its introduction, plus some colour variations. Royal Doulton retired the first Brambly Hedge collection in 1997, but a new collection of figures was introduced in 2000 to celebrate the 20th anniversary of Brambly Hedge.

COLLECTING SNOWMAN FIGURES

Initially, the seasonal appeal of the Snowman tended to limit his collectability, as most purchases were made around Christmas time, and he was more popular in areas which regularly experience snow. Having said this, for some fans the wintry connotations were overshadowed by the inherent quality and humour of the models and there are now keen collectors in sunny Florida as well as in Australia, where beach barbecues are typical Christmas celebrations.

Between 1985 and 1990, young children regularly received the new Snowman models in their Christmas stockings, and the characters have been widely used as holiday decorations. Like the Brambly Hedge models, they were designed to interact, and the little figure of *James*, gazing up in wonder, can be positioned with various Snowman characters, whilst the band works very well as a separate display grouping. There are 19 figures and two musical boxes to collect in the first series,

and as the range was withdrawn in 1994, they can now be quite difficult to locate. In fact, prices have been snowballing, particularly for the figures that were not in production for long, notably *The Snowman Skiing*. The antics of the Snowman were revived in 1999 for a limited edition collection commissioned by Lawleys By Post.

COLLECTING STORYBOOK CHARACTERS

The Beatrix Potter, Brambly Hedge and Snowman stories have already been discussed in some detail, as there are so many figures to collect in each of the categories. However, the Beswick artists have also sought inspiration in other children's stories, some better known than others.

The American author-illustrator, Joan Walsh Anglund, enjoyed quite a vogue in the 1960s following the publication of *A Friend is Someone Who Likes You* (1958). Three of her drawings of cute children with minimal features were modelled by Albert Hallam for the Beswick range in 1969, but they were withdrawn soon after, making them extremely hard to find today.

The bizarre cast of characters from *Alice's Adventures in Wonderland* has offered a lot more scope for collectors. First published in 1865, this classic tale has entertained generations of young readers and inspired many artistic interpretations. In the early 1900s, Doulton's Lambeth artists modelled some fantastic creatures from the tale, notably the pig-like *Rath* from the "Jabberwocky" poem. The Burslem studio designed an extensive series of nursery ware and, more recently, a collection of character jugs based on the original illustrations by Sir John Tenniel, who firmly fixed the appearance of the Wonderland characters in the public imagination. Harry Sales also consulted the Tenniel illustrations in 1973 when designing Beswick's ALICE IN WONDERLAND™.

Curiously the figures inspired by another great children's classic, *The Wind in the Willows*, did not have the same appeal. Christina Thwaites, a young book illustrator, was commissioned to produce designs for a collection of wall plates and tea wares, and her watercolours of *Mr Toad, Ratty, Mole, Badger* and others were interpreted by the Beswick modellers. Four figures were launched in 1987 and two more in 1988 as part of a co-ordinated giftware range with the Royal Albert backstamp, but they were withdrawn in 1989. Consequently *Portly* and *Weasel*, the later introductions, were only made for one year, and will no doubt prove particularly hard to find in the future. Royal Doulton has recently embarked on a new Wind in the Willows collection, which is distributed by Lawleys by Post in a limited edition of 2,000.

With the WIND IN THE WILLOWS™ collection, the Royal Doulton artists have come full circle, reflecting the enthusiasm of their predecessors at Lambeth, notably Francis Pope who modelled two superb figures of *Mr Toad* shortly after the book was published. Obviously storybook characters, particularly animals in human guises, have timeless appeal.

COLLECTING CARTOON CHARACTERS

Cartoon characters, whether they be from animated films or comic book strips, are becoming a popular field for collectors. A major reference book on the subject, together with introductions such as the Hanna Barbera and Disney collections have already generated even more interest. Now is the time to start collecting, if you have not already done so.

The characters from David Hand's Animaland are virtually unknown today, but following their film debut in 1948, they were sufficiently well known to inspire Beswick's first series of cartoon figures. Modelled in 1949 and withdrawn in 1955, *Zimmy the Lion* and his seven friends now have a different kind of notoriety, stealing the show when they come up for auction.

In contrast, Mickey Mouse is the best known cartoon character in the world. Within a year of his 1928 screen debut in *Steamboat Willie*, his image was being used to endorse children's products, and by the 1950s there were more than 3,000 different Mickey Mouse items, including plates, dolls, watches and clothes. With all this merchandising activity, it is not surprising that the Beswick studio sought a license for portraying Mickey and his friends in ceramic.

A range of nursey ware was launched in 1954, along with figures of *Mickey* and his girlfriend *Minnie*, *Pluto* his dog and his crazy friends *Goofy* and *Donald Duck*. Characters from some of Walt Disney's feature-length cartoons completed the original WALT DISNEY CHARACTERS™ set of 12 figures. *Peter Pan*, the newest Disney hit in 1953, inspired four characters, *Peter* himself, *Tinkerbell*, *Smee* and *Nana*, whilst the classic *Pinocchio* (1940) provided the puppet hero and his insect conscience *Jiminy Cricket*. Surprisingly only *Thumper* was modelled from another favourite film, *Bambi* (1942), although the fawn appears on the tableware designs. The response to the initial Disney collection encouraged the Beswick factory to launch a second set the following year, featuring *Snow White and the Seven Dwarfs* from Disney's first feature symphony. All the Disney characterisations are superb, making them extremely desirable amongst collectors of Beswick and Disneyana and they are all hard to find, even though they were produced until 1967.

The 1960s saw the rise of a new Disney star, Winnie the Pooh, who became a very popular merchandising character after his cartoon debut in 1966. The Beswick factory was quick off the mark, launching an initial collection of six characters from the film in 1968, followed by two more in 1971. "The Bear of Little Brain" originated in bedtime stories about nursery toys told by A. A. Milne to his son Christopher Robin in the 1920s, and he was visualised in the resulting books by the illustrator E. H. Shepard. To celebrate the 70th anniversary of the first *Winnie the Pooh* book, Royal Doulton launched a second series of figures in 1996 and these have been a great success. Royal Doulton continue to work closely with the Walt Disney company today and they have launched two exciting figurine collections featuring Disney *Princesses* and *Villains* exclusively for sale in the Disney stores. The other new Disney collections have been distributed through specialist china shops, notably the *101 Dalmatians* series, which was inspired by the live action film, and the second series of *Snow White and the Seven Dwarfs*, which was prompted by the 60th anniversary of the film. A new Disney series featuring Mickey Mouse and his gang, was launched during 1998 so don't miss the opportunity to add these to your cartoon collection.

The massive marketing campaigns for Disney characters have made them household names all over the world. British cartoon characters, by comparison, are less well known internationally. The *Daily Express* newspaper was slow to capitalise on the success of *Rupert the Bear*, who has been the star of their children's comic strip since 1920. Originated by Mary Tourtel, the Rupert stories were enlivened by Alfred Bestall who took over the daily drawings in 1935. Rupert enjoys the most extraordinary adventures with his friends Bill the Badger, Algy Pug and Pong-Ping, always returning safely to his comfortable family home in Nutwood. Rupert Bear annuals sold in millions from the mid 1930s, and his exploits were adapted for TV in the 1970s, but his following is essentially British. No doubt it was for this reason that the five figures in the original RUPERT THE BEAR™ collection, designed by Harry Sales in 1980, were relatively short lived. However, the second Rupert Bear collection, launched in 1998, is proving very popular with Lawleys By Post customers.

A similar fate befell the NORMAN THELWELL™ figures, which were in production from 1981 to 1989. Norman Thelwell was a humorous illustrator for *Punch* magazine, who made his reputation with comical observations of young riders and their mounts. *Angels on Horseback*, published in 1957, was the first compilation of his successful cartoons, and many other popular books followed. Thelwell worked closely with Harry Sales to create the most effective figures, both in ceramic and resin, and the results are guaranteed to raise a smile without breaking the bank.

After a gap of nearly 15 years, famous British cartoon characters are back on the drawing board at the Royal Doulton studios once again. *Denis the Menace* and *Desperate Dan*, stars of the long-established children's comics, *The Beano* and *The Dandy*, have been immortalised as character jugs. This is the first time large-size character jugs have been used for portraying cartoons, although there are similarities to the set of six THUNDERBIRDS™ busts modelled by jug designer Bill Harper to celebrate the 30th anniversary of this children's TV show in 1992.

COLLECTING CHARACTER ANIMALS

In the 1880s Doulton's first artist, George Tinworth, was modelling groups of mice engaged in popular human pastimes, and nearly a century later Kitty MacBride did much the same thing with her *Happy Mice*. The appeal of these anthropomorphic creatures is timeless, and collectors have responded with enthusiasm from Victorian times to the present day.

Admittedly, developing a taste for Tinworth's sense of humour will prove very expensive, with models costing several hundreds of pounds each, but the KITTY MACBRIDE™ whimsical mice are still relatively affordable.

Kitty MacBride was a writer and illustrator who began to model little clay figures of mice in 1960. Initially they were sold through a London dealer, but when she could not keep up with the demand she asked the Beswick factory to produce 11 of them commercially, which they did between 1975 and 1983.

The Beswick studio has had a considerable reputation for character animals since the launch of the Beatrix Potter collection in 1948. However, the modellers have not only interpreted illustrations from famous books, from time to time they have envisaged their own comical creatures. Albert Hallam was responsible for a succession of animals with human expressions in the late 1960s. Similar humanising traits can be found in the LITTLE LIKEABLES™ collection, which was produced briefly in the mid 1980s. Robert Tabbenor's animals play up the humour of their situation, notably the carefree frog, *Watching the World Go By*, whilst Diane Griffiths takes a more sentimental approach, using human feelings to describe her cartoon-like animals.

The fun has continued in recent years with a collection of *Footballing Felines*, produced in 1999, and the on-going series of *English Country Folk*, depicting appropriate animals with human manners and costumes. However, the last laugh is reserved for the *Pig Promenade*. The absurdity of nine different breeds of pigs playing musical instruments makes this one of the most hilarious series of character animals.

MAKING STORYBOOK CHARACTERS

All the current storybook characters are made at the John Beswick factory in Longton, which became part of the Royal Doulton group in 1969. They have over fifty years' experience in the production of humorous figures and character animals, and essentially the methods have not changed since the earliest days of the Beatrix Potter figures.

First of all the designer has to familiarise himself thoroughly with the character to be portrayed, reading the story and studying the illustration. Having chosen the most suitable pose for interpretation in ceramic, he will produce reference drawings for the modeller. Often he can only see one side of the character in the original illustration, so he has to improvise for his three-dimensional model.

In consultation with the designer, the modeller will create the figure in modelling clay, and if satisfactory, a set of master moulds will be made in plaster of Paris. The number of mould parts will depend on the complexity of the figure, and sometimes the head and arms have to be moulded separately. Two or three prototype figures will be cast from the master mould for colour trials and subsequent approval by the original artist or his agent.

In the case of the Beatrix Potter figures, all the models are scrutinised by the licensing agents, Copyrights, working on behalf of Miss Potter's original publishers,

Frederick Warne. Raymond Briggs, who was responsible for the Snowman, is generally quite relaxed about letting experts in other media interpret his drawings. He thought Royal Doultons models were marvellous and really captured the spirit of the story, although he maintained he would "jolly well say so" if he thought they had got it wrong! Jill Barklem, the creator of Brambly Hedge, likes to get very involved in the licensing of her characters, and design manager Harry Sales spent a lot of time working with her on the finer points of detail. Sometimes slight modifications need to be made to the model or the colour scheme before the figure is approved by all concerned.

The next stage is to produce plaster of Paris working moulds from the master, and supplies are sent to the casting department. An earthenware body is used to cast all the character figures produced at the John Beswick studio, and it is poured into the mould in liquid form, known as slip. The moisture in the slip is absorbed into the plaster of Paris moulds and a "skin" of clay forms the interior.

Once the clay has set to the required thickness, the excess clay is poured out and the mould is carefully dismantled. Any separate mould parts, such as projecting arms, will be joined on at this stage using slip as an adhesive, and the seams will be gently sponged away. The figure is then allowed to dry slowly before it goes for its first firing. The high temperature in the kiln drives out the moisture in the body and the figure shrinks by about 1/12th of its original size, forming a hard "biscuit" body.

Skilled decorators will paint the figure, using special under-glaze ceramic colours. They work from an approved colour sample and great care is taken to match the colours to the original book illustrations. A second firing hardens on the colour before the figure is coated with a solution of liquid glaze. When the figure is fired in the glost kiln, it emerges with a shiny transparent finish which enhances and permanently protects the vibrant colours underneath. After a final inspection, the figures are dispatched to china shops all over the world where they will capture the hearts of collectors young and old.

RESIN FIGURES

Several collectables manufacturers began experimenting with new sculptural materials in the 1980s and developed different types of resin bodies that allow more intricately modelled detail than conventional ceramic processes. Royal Doulton launched its new "bonded ceramic body" in 1984, and two storybook collections were included in its Beswick Studio Sculptures, as the range was known. Seven subjects were chosen from the *Tales of Beatrix Potter* and two from the Thelwell series. Production was short-lived, despite the minute detailing of the animals' fur and the tiny pebbles and grasses in their habitat, which would have been impossible to achieve in traditional earthenware. Royal Doulton ceased production of resin at the end of 1985, but designs have been commissioned from resin specialists, notably the *Paddington Bear* and *St. Tiggywinkles* series.

COLLECTORS CLUBS AND GUILDS

Royal Doulton International Collectors Club

Founded in 1980, the Royal Doulton International Collectors Club provides an information service on all aspects of the company's products, past and present. A club magazine, *Gallery*, is published four times a year with information on new products and current events that will keep the collector up-to-date on the happenings in the world of Royal Doulton. Upon joining the club, each new member will receive a free gift and invitations to special events and exclusive offers.

To join the Royal Doulton Collectors Club, please contact your local stockist, or contact the club directly at the address or telephone numbers below:

Minton House
London Road, Stoke-on-Trent
Staffordshire ST4 7QD, England
Telephone:
    U.K.: (01782) 292127
    U.S.A. and Canada: 1-800-747-3045 (toll free)
    Australia: 011-800-142624 (toll free)
Fax: U.K.: (01782) 292099
Attn.: Jill Daniels

Royal Crown Derby Collectors Guild

The Royal Crown Derby Collectors Guild was established in 1994 to establish contact with Royal Crown Derby Collectors. Membership entitles the collector to a yearly subscription to the quarterly Royal Crown Derby magazine, membership gift and free admission for the member to the Royal Crown Derby Visitor Centre.

To join the Royal Crown Derby Collectors Guild, please contact the guild at the address or telephone number below:

Royal Crown Derby
194 Osmaston Road, Derby DE23 8JZ
Tel: (44) 1332 712846 Fax: (44) 1332 712899
Attn: Jackie Banks

Caithness Glass Paperweight Collectors Society
Caithness Glass International Paperweight Collectors Society

Formed in 1997, by Colin Terris, the society is the clearing house for all information on Caithness Glass Paperweights. Membership of the society entitles the collector to receive *Reflections*, the society's twice yearly magazine, plus three newsletters and a personal tour of the paperweight studios in Perth, Scotland, if you are ever in the area. An annual International Convention is held in Scotland in October.

To join the Caithness Glass Paperweight Collectors Society, please contact the society at one of the addresses or telephone numbers below:

In the U.K. and International
Caithness Glass Paperweight Collectors Society
Caithness Glass Inc.
Inveralmond, Perth PH1 3TZ, Scotland
Tel.: (44) (0) 1738 637373
Fax: (44) (0) 1738 622494

In the U.S.A.
Caithness Glass Paperweight Collectors Society
Caithness Glass Inc.
141 Lanza Avenue, Building No. 12
Garfield, N.J. 07026, U.S.A.
Tel.: 973-340-3330
Fax: 973-340-9415

COLLECTOR CLUB CHAPTERS

Chapters of the RDICC have formed across North America and are worthy of consideration for collectors in those areas.

Detroit Chapter
Frank Americk, President
1771 Brody, Allen Park, MI 48101

Edmonton Chapter
Mildred's Collectibles
6813 104 Street, Edmonton, AB T6H 2L5

New England Chapter
Robert Hicks, President
Lee Piper, Vice-President
Michael Lynch, Secretary
Scott Reichenberg, Treasurer
E-mail: doingantiq@aol.com

Northern California Chapter
Edward L. Khachadourian, President
P.O. Box 214, Moraga, CA 94556-0214
Tel.: (925) 376-2221 Fax: (925) 376-3581
E-mail: khach@pacbell.net

Northwest, Bob Haynes, Chapter
Alan Matthew, President
15202 93rd Place NE, Bothell, WA 98011
Tel.: (425) 488-9604

Ohio Chapter
Reg Morris, President
Dick Maschmeier, Treasurer
5556 Whitehaven Avenue,
North Olmstead, Ohio 44070
Tel.: (216) 779-5554

Rochester Chapter
Judith L. Trost President
103 Garfield Street, Rochester, NY 14611
Tel.: (716) 436-3321

Western Pennsylvania Chapter
John Re, President
9589 Parkedge Drive, Allison Park, PA 15101
Tel.: (412) 366-0201 Fax: (412) 366-2558

VISITOR CENTRES

Royal Doulton Visitor Centre

Opened in the summer of 1996, the Royal Doulton Visitor Centre houses the largest collection of Royal Doulton figurines in the world. Demonstration areas offer the collector a first hand insight on how figurines are assembled and decorated. Also at the Visitor Centre is a cinema showing a 20 minute video on the history of Royal Doulton, plus a restaurant, and a retail shop offering both best quality ware and slight seconds.

Factory tours may be booked, Monday to Friday, at the Visitor Centre.

Nile Street, Burslem
Stoke-on-Trent, ST6 2AJ, England
Tel.: (01782) 292434
Fax: (01782) 292424
Attn.: Yvonne Wood

Royal Doulton John Beswick Studios

Tours of the John Beswick Factory and Museum are available Monday to Thursday by appointment only. Please book in advance.

Gold Street, Longton
Stoke-on-Trent, ST3 2JP, England
Tel.: (01782) 291213
Fax: (01782) 291279
Attn.: Margaret Burton

Royal Crown Derby Visitor Centre

Opened in the spring of 1998, the Visitor Centre was created to provide an insight into the tradition, history amd skills that go into making Royal Crown Derby collectables. The centre houses the largest collection of Royal Crown Derby seen anywhere in the world, a demonstration area for skilled Royal Crown Derby artists and crafts people, restaurants, and shops.

Factory tours may be booked Monday to Friday at the centre, with advance bookings suggested.

194 Osmaston Road
Derby, DE23 8JZ, England
Tel.: (01332) 712841
Fax: (01332) 712899
Attn.: Stella Birks

Caithness Glass Visitor Centre

The Visitor Centre is home to the largest public display of Caithness Glass paperweights. Over 1200 designs are on display. A special viewing gallery enables visitors to watch the complete paperweight making process.

Inveralmond
Perth, PH1 3TZ, Scotland
Tel.: (44) (0)1738 637373
Fax: (44) (0)1738 622494

Factory Shops

Royal Doulton Visitor Centre
Nile Street, Burslem
Stoke-on-Trent ST6 2AJ, England
Tel.: (01782) 292451

Royal Doulton Group Factory Shop
Lawley Street, Longton
Stoke-on-Trent ST3 2PH, England
Tel.: (01782) 291172

Royal Doulton Factory Shop
Minton House, London Road
Stoke-on-Trent ST4 7QD, England
Tel.: (01782) 292121

Royal Doulton Factory Shop
Leek New Road, Baddeley Green,
Stoke-on-Trent ST2 7HS, England
Tel.: (01782) 291700

Royal Doulton Factory Shop
Victoria Road, Fenton,
Stoke-on-Trent ST4 2PJ, England
Tel.: (01782) 291869

Beswick Factory Shop
Barford Street, Longton,
Stoke-on-Trent ST3 2JP, England
Tel.: (01782) 291237

Web Site and E-mail Addresses

Sites: www.royal-doulton.com
www.caithnessglass.co.uk
E-mail:
Clubs: icc@royal-doulton.com
Visitor Centre: visitor@royal-doulton.com
Consumer Enquiries: enquiries@royal-doulton.com
Museum Curator: heritage@royal-doulton.com
Lawleys by Post: lbp@royal-doulton.com

WHERE TO BUY

Discontinued Doulton collectables can be found in antique shops, markets, auctions, shows and fairs. Specialist dealers in Royal Doulton collectables attend many of the events listed below.

For Auction happenings it is necessary to subscribe to Auction Houses that hold 20th Century or Doulton Auctions.

UNITED KINGDOM
Auction Houses

BBR Auctions
Elsecar Heritage Centre
Nr. Barnsley
South Yorkshire S74 8HJ, England
Tel.: (01226) 745156
Fax: (01226) 351561
Attn: Alan Blakeman

Bonhams
65-69 Lots Road, Chelsea
London SW10 0RN, England
Tel.: (0207) 393-3900
Fax: (0207) 393-3906
www.bonhams.com
Attn: Neil Grenyer

Christie's South Kensington
85 Old Brompton Road
London SW7 3LD, England
Tel.: (0207) 581 7611
Fax: (0207) 321-3321
www.christies.com
Attn: Michael Jeffrey

Potteries Specialist Auctions
271 Waterloo Road
Stoke-on-Trent
Staffordshire ST6 3HR, England
Tel.: (01782) 286622
Fax: (01782) 213777
Attn: Steve Anderson

Louis Taylor
Britannia House
10 Town Road, Hanley,
Stoke-on-Trent ST1 2QG
England
Tel.: (01782) 21411
Fax: (01782) 215283
Attn: Clive Hillier

Phillips
101 New Bond Street
London W1Y 0AS, England
Tel.: (0207) 629-6602
Fax: (0207) 629-8876
www.phillips-auctions.com
Attn: Mark Oliver

Sotheby's
34-35 New Bond Street
London W1A 2AA, England
Tel.: (0207) 293-5000
Fax: (0207) 293-5989
www.sothebys.com
Attn: Christina Donaldson

Sotheby's Sussex
Summers Place
Billingshurst, Sussex RH14 9AF
England
Tel.: (01403) 833500
Fax: (01403) 833699

Thomson Roddick & Laurie
60 Whitesands
Dumfries DG1 2RS
Scotland
Tel.: (01387) 255366
Fax: (01387) 266236
Attn: Sybelle Medcalf

Peter Wilson Auctioneers
Victoria Gallery, Market Street
Nantwich, Cheshire CW5 5DG
England
Tel.: (01270) 623878
Fax: (01270) 610508
Attn: Stella Ashbrook or
      Robert Stone

Antique Fairs

Doulton and Beswick Collectors Fair
National Motorcycle Museum, Meriden, Birmingham
Usually March and August.
For information on times and dates:
Doulton and Beswick Dealers Association
Tel.: (0208) 303 3316

Doulton and Beswick Collectors Fair
Dorking. Usually in October.
For information on times and location:
UK Fairs Ltd., 10 Wilford Bridge Spur,
Melton,Woodbridge, Suffolk, IP12 1RJ
Tel.: (01394) 386663

20th Century Fairs
266 Glossop Road, Sheffield S10 2HS, England
Usually the last week in May or the first week in June.
For information on times and dates:
Tel.: (0114) 275-0333
Fax: (0114) 275-4443

International Antique & Collectors Fair
Newark, Nottinghamshire
Usually six fairs annually.
For information on times and dates:
International Antique & Collectors Fair Ltd.
P.O. Box 100, Newark, Nottinghamshire, NG2 1DJ
Tel.: (01636) 702326

West London Wade Beswick & Doulton Fair
Brunel University, Kingston Lane,
Uxbridge, Middlesex
For information on times and dates:
B & D Fairs, P.O. Box 273, Uxbridge
Middlesex, UB9 4LP
Tel.: (01895) 834694 or 834357

Yesterdays Doulton Fair
Usually November.
For information on times and location:
Doulton and Beswick Dealers Association
Tel.: (0208) 303-3316

London Markets

Alfie's Antique Market
13-25 Church Street, London
Tuesday - Saturday

Camden Passage Market
Upper Street, London N1
Wednesday and Saturday

New Caledonia Market
Bermondsey Square, London
Friday morning

Portobello Road Market
Portobello Road, London
Saturday

UNITED STATES
Auction Houses

Christie's East
219 East 67th Street
New York, NY 10021
Tel.: (212) 606-0400
www.christies.com
Attn: Timothy Luke

Sotheby's Arcade Auctions
1334 York Avenue
New York, NY 10021
Tel.: (212) 606-7000
www.sothebys.com
Attn: Andrew Cheney

Collectable Shows

Atlantique City
New Atlantic City Convention Centre
Atlantic City, NJ
Usually March and October
For information on times and dates:
Brimfield and Associates
P.O. Box 1800, Ocean City, NJ 08226
Tel.: (609) 926-1800
www.atlantiquecity.com

Florida Doulton Convention & Sale
Sheraton Fort Lauderdale
1825 Griffin Road
Fort Lauderdale, Florida
Usually mid-January
For information on times and dates:
Pascoe and Company
932 Ponce De Leon Blvd., Coral Gables, FL 33134
Tel.: (305) 445-3229

O'Hare National Antiques Show & Sale
Rosemont Convention Centre,
Chicago, IL.
Usually April, August and November
For information on times and dates:
Manor House Shows Inc.
P.O. Box 7320, Fort Lauderdale, Florida 33338
Tel.: (954) 563-6747

Royal Doulton Convention & Sale
John S. Knight Convention Centre
77 E. Mill Street, Akron, Ohio 44308
Usually August.
For information on times and dates:
Colonial House Productions
182 Front Street, Berea, Ohio 44017
Tel.: (800) 344-9299

CANADA
Auction Houses

Maynards
415 West 2nd Avenue
Vancouver, British Columbia V5Y 1E3
Tel.: (604) 876-1311

Ritchie's
288 King Street East, Toronto, Ontario M5A 1K4
Tel.: (416) 364-1864   Fax: (416) 364-0704
Attn: Caroline Kaiser

Collectable Shows

Canadian Art & Collectibles Show & Sale
Kitchener Memorial Auditorium, Kitchener, Ontario.
Usually early May.
For information on times and location:
George or Jackie Benninger
P.O. Box 130, Durham, Ontario N0G 1R0
Tel.: (519) 369-6950

Canadian Doulton & Collectable Fair
Toronto, Ontario.
Usually early September.
For information on times and location:
George or Jackie Benninger
P.O. Box 130, Durham, Ontario N0G 1R0
Tel.: (519) 369-6950

FURTHER READING

Storybook Figurines

The Charlton Standard Catalogue of Bunnykins by Jean Dale and Louise Irvine
The Charlton Standard Catalogue of Border Fine Arts Storybook Figurines by Marylin Sweet
Cartoon Classics and other Character Figures by Louise Irvine
Royal Doulton Bunnykins Figures by Louise Irvine
Bunnykins Collectors Book by Louise Irvine
Beatrix Potter Figures and Giftware edited by Louise Irvine
The Beswick Price Guide by Harvey May
Brambly Hedge Collectors Book by Louise Irvine

Animals, Figures and Character Jugs

Royal Doulton Figures by Desmond Eyles, Louise Irvine and Valerie Baynton
The Charlton Standard Catalogue of Beswick Animals by Diane & John Callow
  and Marilyn & Peter Sweet
The Charlton Standard Catalogue of Royal Doulton Animals by Jean Dale
The Charlton Standard Catalogue of Royal Doulton Beswick Figurines by Jean Dale
The Charlton Standard Catalogue of Royal Doulton Beswick Jugs by Jean Dale
Collecting Character and Toby Jugs by Jocelyn Lukins
Collecting Doulton Animals by Jocelyn Lukins
Doulton Flambé Animals by Jocelyn Lukins
The Character Jug Collectors Handbook by Kevin Pearson
The Doulton Figure Collectors Handbook by Kevin Pearson

General

The Charlton Standard Catalogue of Beswick Pottery by Diane and John Callow
Discovering Royal Doulton by Michael Doulton
The Doulton Story by Paul Atterbury and Louise Irvine
Royal Doulton Series Ware by Louise Irvine (Vols. 1-5)
Limited Edition Loving Cups by Louise Irvine and Richard Dennis
Doulton for the Collector by Jocelyn Lukins
Doulton Kingsware Flasks by Jocelyn Lukins
Doulton Burslem Advertising Wares by Jocelyn Lukins
Doulton Lambeth Advertising Ware by Jocelyn Lukins
The Doulton Lambeth Wares by Desmond Eyles
The Doulton Burslem Wares by Desmond Eyles
Hannah Barlow by Peter Rose
George Tinworth by Peter Rose
Sir Henry Doulton Biography by Edmund Gosse
Phillips Collectors Guide by Catherine Braithwaite
Royal Doulton by Jennifer Queree
John Beswick: A World of Imagination. Catalogue reprint (1950-1996)
Royal Doulton by Julie McKeown

Magazines and Newsletters

Rabbitting On (Bunnykins Newsletter) Contact Leah Selig: 2 Harper Street, Merrylands 2160
  New South Wales, Australia. Tel./Fax 61 2 9637 2410 (International), 02 637 2410 (Australia)

Collect It! Contact subscription department at: P.O. Box 3658, Bracknell, Berkshire RG12 7XZ
  Telephone: (1344) 868280 or e-mail: collectit@dialpipex.com

Collecting Doulton Magazine, Contact Barry Hill, P.O. Box 310, Richmond, Surrey

Doulton News, published by Thorndon Antiques & Fine China Ltd., edited by David Harcourt
  P.O. Box 12-076 (109 Molesworth Street), Wellington, New Zealand

Beswick Quarterly (Beswick Newsletter) Contact Laura J. Rock-Smith: 10 Holmes Ct., Sayville,
  N.Y. 11782-2408, U.S.A. Tel./Fax 516-589-9027

Royal Doulton
Brambly Hedge

FIGURES

1 Lord Woodmouse DBH4
2 Primrose Woodmouse DBH8
3 Lady Woodmouse DBH5
4 Wilfred Toadflax DBH7
5 Catkin DBH12
6 Flax Weaver DBH20
7 Lily Weaver DBH19
8 Clover DBH16
9 Mrs. Toadflax DBH11
10 Mr. Toadflax DBH10
11 Poppy Eyebright DBH1
12 Dusty Dogwood DBH6
13 Mrs. Apple DBH3
14 Mr. Apple DBH2
15 Mrs. Crustybread DBH15
16 Conker DBH21
17 Mr. Saltapple DBH24
18 Mrs. Saltapple DBH25
19 Old Mrs. Eyebright DBH9
20 Wilfred Entertains DBH23
21 Primrose Entertains DBH22

Advertisement for Brambly Hedge Figurines

ALICE IN WONDERLAND

EARTHENWARE SERIES 1973-1983
EARTHENWARE SERIES 1998 to date
RESIN SERIES 1997-1997

ALICE IN WONDERLAND

EARTHENWARE SERIES 1973-1983

2476
ALICE™
Style One

Designer:	Albert Hallam and Graham Tongue
Height:	4 ¾", 12.1 cm
Colour:	Dark blue dress, white apron with red trim
Issued:	1973 - 1983
Series:	Alice

Beswick	Price			
Number	U.S. $	Can. $	U.K. £	Aust. $
2476	450.00	625.00	250.00	575.00

2477
WHITE RABBIT™
Style One

Designer:	Graham Tongue
Height:	4 ¾", 12.1 cm
Colour:	White rabbit wearing a brown coat, yellow waistcoat
Issued:	1973 - 1983
Series:	Alice

Beswick	Price			
Number	U.S. $	Can. $	U.K. £	Aust. $
2477	500.00	650.00	250.00	600.00

2478
MOCK TURTLE™

Designer:	Graham Tongue
Height:	4 ¼", 10.8 cm
Colour:	Browns and grey
Issued:	1973 - 1983
Series:	Alice

Beswick Number	Price			
	U.S. $	Can. $	U.K. £	Aust. $
2478	300.00	450.00	175.00	425.00

2479
MAD HATTER™
Style One

Designer:	Albert Hallam
Height:	4 ¼", 10.8 cm
Colour:	Burgundy coat, yellow and blue checked trousers, yellow and red bowtie, grey hat
Issued:	1973 - 1983
Series:	Alice

Beswick Number	Price			
	U.S. $	Can. $	U.K. £	Aust. $
2479	325.00	475.00	225.00	475.00

2480
CHESHIRE CAT™
Style One

Designer:	Albert Hallam and Graham Tongue
Height:	1 ½", 3.8 cm
Colour:	Tabby cat
Issued:	1973 - 1982
Series:	Alice

Beswick Number	Price			
	U.S. $	Can. $	U.K. £	Aust. $
2480	600.00	800.00	425.00	775.00

2485
GRYPHON™

Designer:	Albert Hallam
Height:	3 ¼", 8.3 cm
Colour:	Browns and greens
Issued:	1973 - 1983
Series:	Alice

Beswick	Price			
Number	U.S. $	Can. $	U.K. £	Aust. $
2485	175.00	250.00	100.00	225.00

2489
KING OF HEARTS™

Designer:	Graham Tongue
Height:	3 ¾", 9.5 cm
Colour:	Burgundy, yellow, white, blue and green
Issued:	1973 - 1983
Series:	Alice

Beswick	Price			
Number	U.S. $	Can. $	U.K. £	Aust. $
2489	125.00	175.00	75.00	175.00

2490
QUEEN OF HEARTS™
Style One

Designer:	Graham Tongue
Height:	4", 10.1 cm
Colour:	Blue, green, yellow, white and burgundy
Issued:	1973 - 1983
Series:	Alice

Beswick	Price			
Number	U.S. $	Can. $	U.K. £	Aust. $
2490	125.00	175.00	75.00	175.00

2545
DODO™
Style One

Designer:	David Lyttleton
Height:	4", 10.1 cm
Colour:	Browns and greens
Issued:	1975 - 1983
Series:	Alice

ALICE SERIES
"Dodo"
BESWICK
MADE IN ENGLAND
© ROYAL DOULTON TABLEWARE LTD. 1975
REGISTRATION APPLIED FOR.

Beswick	*Price*			
Number	*U.S. $*	*Can. $*	*U.K. £*	*Aust. $*
2545	250.00	375.00	165.00	325.00

2546
FISH FOOTMAN™

Designer:	David Lyttleton
Height:	4 ¾", 14.6 cm
Colour:	Blue, gold, white and brown
Issued:	1975 - 1983
Series:	Alice

ALICE SERIES
"Fish Footman"
BESWICK
MADE IN ENGLAND
© ROYAL DOULTON TABLEWARE LTD 1975
REGISTRATION APPLIED FOR

Beswick	*Price*			
Number	*U.S. $*	*Can. $*	*U.K. £*	*Aust. $*
2546	275.00	450.00	200.00	500.00

2547
FROG FOOTMAN™

Designer:	David Lyttleton
Height:	4 ¼", 10.8 cm
Colour:	Maroon jacket with yellow trim, blue trousers
Issued:	1975 - 1983
Series:	Alice

ALICE SERIES
"Frog Footman"
BESWICK
MADE IN ENGLAND
© ROYAL DOULTON TABLEWARE LTD 1975
REGISTRATION APPLIED FOR

Beswick	*Price*			
Number	*U.S. $*	*Can. $*	*U.K. £*	*Aust. $*
2547	375.00	575.00	275.00	525.00

ALICE IN WONDERLAND

EARTHENWARE SERIES 1998 to date

LC001
THE MAD HATTER'S TEA PARTY™

Modeller:	Martyn Alcock
Size:	5" x 8 ½", 12.7 x 21.6 cm
Colour:	Green, yellow, red and blue
Issued:	1998 in a limited edition of 1,998
Series:	1. Alice's Adventures
	2. Tableau

Beswick	Price			
Number	U.S. $	Can. $	U.K. £	Aust. $
LC001	275.00	375.00	175.00	375.00

Note: Issued to commemorate the centenary of Lewis Carroll's death.

LC002
ALICE™
Style Three

Modeller:	Martyn Alcock
Size:	4 ½", 11.9 cm
Colour:	Pink dress, white apron
Issued:	1999 in a limited edition of 2,500
Series:	Alice's Adventures

Beswick	Price			
Number	U.S. $	Can. $	U.K. £	Aust. $
LC002	Pair with Cheshire Cat (Style Three)	—	—	90.00	—

Note: Issued, numbered and sold as a pair with Cheshire Cat (Style Three).

LC003
CHESHIRE CAT™
Style Three

Modeller:	Martyn Alcock
Size:	3 ½", 8.9 cm
Colour:	Ginger striped cat with green eyes
Issued:	1999 in a limited edition of 2,500
Series:	Alice's Adventures

Beswick	Price			
Number	U.S. $	Can. $	U.K. £	Aust. $
LC003	Pair with Alice (Style Three)	—	—	90.00	—

Note: Issued, numbered and sold as a pair with Alice (Style Three).

LC004
QUEEN OF HEARTS™
Style Three

Modeller:	Martyn Alcock
Size:	5 ¼", 13.3 cm
Colour:	Red, dark blue, yellow and pink
Issued:	2000 in a limited edition of 2,500
Series:	Alice's Adventures

Beswick Number	Price			
	U.S. $	*Can. $*	*U.K. £*	*Aust. $*
LC004	—	—	50.00	—

ALICE IN WONDERLAND

RESIN SERIES 1997-1997

ALICE™
Style Two

Designer:	Adrian Hughes
Height:	4", 10.1 cm
Colour:	Pale blue and white dress, red and white toadstool, green base
Issued:	1997 - 1997

Doulton	Price			
Number	U.S. $	Can. $	U.K. £	Aust. $
—	40.00	60.00	25.00	60.00
Complete Set (6 pcs.)	225.00	350.00	150.00	350.00

CHESHIRE CAT™
Style Two

Designer:	Adrian Hughes
Height:	4", 10.1 cm
Colour:	Orange striped cat, blue butterfly, red ladybird, brown tree stump, green base
Issued:	1997 - 1997

Doulton	Price			
Number	U.S. $	Can. $	U.K. £	Aust. $
—	40.00	60.00	25.00	60.00

DODO™
Style Two

Designer:	Adrian Hughes
Height:	4", 10.1 cm
Colour:	White bird with blue wing tips, yellow head and black beak
Issued:	1997 - 1997

Doulton	Price			
Number	U.S. $	Can. $	U.K. £	Aust. $
—	40.00	60.00	25.00	60.00

Note: The *Alice In Wonderland* resin series does not carry a backstamp. It was sold as a set through Lawleys By Post.

MAD HATTER™
Style Two

Designer:	Adrian Hughes
Height:	4", 10.1 cm
Colour:	Brown trousers and top hat, green jacket, blue waistcoat, green base
Issued:	1997 - 1997

Doulton Number	Price			
	U.S. $	*Can. $*	*U.K. £*	*Aust. $*
—	40.00	60.00	25.00	60.00

QUEEN OF HEARTS™
Style Two

Designer:	Adrian Hughes
Height:	4", 10.1 cm
Colour:	Red coat trimmed with white, white dress with red and black design, black and red crown
Issued:	1997 - 1997

Doulton Number	Price			
	U.S. $	*Can. $*	*U.K. £*	*Aust. $*
—	40.00	60.00	25.00	60.00

WHITE RABBIT™
Style Two

Designer:	Adrian Hughes
Height:	4", 10.1 cm
Colour:	White rabbit with brown jacket and green waistcoat, green base
Issued:	1997 - 1997

Doulton Number	Price			
	U.S. $	*Can. $*	*U.K. £*	*Aust. $*
—	40.00	60.00	25.00	60.00

BEATRIX POTTER
FIGURINES

BEATRIX POTTER BACKSTAMPS

BP-1 BESWICK GOLD CIRCLE AND BESWICK GOLD PARALLEL LINES ISSUED 1948 TO 1954

BP-1 was the original Beswick Beatrix Potter backstamp; it was used on 21 figures plus one variation between 1948 and 1954. In addition, there are reports that it may have been used in error on *Tommy Brock*. There are two varieties of this backstamp.

BP-1a (gold circle). The first variety has the words "Beswick" and "England" forming a circle; a copyright notice may or may not appear. This variety was used on 19 figures; plus one variation and the *Tommy Brock* error.

The following is a list of the 19 figures on which the BP-1a backstamp was used:

Benjamin Bunny, first version
Duchess, style one
Flopsy, Mopsy and Cottontail
Foxy Whiskered Gentleman, first version
Hunca Munca
Jemima Puddle-Duck, first version, first variation
Johnny Town-Mouse
Lady Mouse
Little Pig Robinson, first variation
Miss Moppet, first variation
Mr. Jeremy Fisher, first and second variations
Mrs. Tiggy-Winkle, first version, first variation
Mrs. Tittlemouse
Peter Rabbit, first version, first variation
Ribby
Samuel Whiskers
Squirrel Nutkin, first version, first variation
Timmy Tiptoes, first variation
Timmy Willie From Johnny Town-Mouse
Tom Kitten, first version, first variation
Tommy Brock, first version, first variation

BP-1a Beswick Gold Circle

BP-1b (gold parallel lines). The second variety has the words "Beswick" and "England" arranged in parallel lines, "Beswick" atop "England"; the word "Copyright" appears in script. This variety, BP-1b, was used on two figures:

Mrs. Rabbit, first version, first variation
The Tailor of Gloucester, first version

It was also used in error on a few other figures, including *Benjamin Bunny*. An illustration of this backstamp was not available at press time.

BP-2 BESWICK GOLD OVAL ISSUED 1955 TO 1972

The gold oval was in use for 18 years, between 1955 and 1972, on 38 figures plus 4 versions/variations. *Pig-Wig*, introduced in 1972, was the last in line for the gold oval backstamp, and in some quarters they still doubt that it officially exists.

The following is a list of figures that can found with a BP-2 backstamp:

Amiable Guinea-Pig, style one
Anna Maria
Apply Dappley, first version
Aunt Pettitoes
Benjamin Bunny, first and second versions
Cecily Parsley, first version
Cousin Ribby
Duchess (with flowers)
Flopsy, Mopsy and Cottontail
Foxy Whiskered Gentleman, first version
Goody Tiptoes
Hunca Munca
Jemima Puddle-Duck, first version, first variation
Johnny Town-Mouse
Lady Mouse
Little Pig Robinson, first variation
Miss Moppet, first variation
Mr. Benjamin Bunny, first version
Mr. Jeremy Fisher, first version, first variation
Mrs. Flopsy Bunny
Mrs. Rabbit, first version
Mrs. Tiggy-Winkle, first verion, first and second variations
Mrs. Tittlemouse, style one
Old Mr. Brown
Old Woman Who Lived in a Shoe, The
Peter Rabbit, first version, first variation
Pickles
Pigling Bland, first variation
Pig-Wig
Ribby
Samuel Whiskers
Squirrel Nutkin, first version, first variation
Tabitha Twitchit, first variation
Tailor of Gloucester, first version
Timmy Tiptoes, first and second variations
Timmy Willie From Johnny Town-Mouse
Tom Kitten, first version, first variation
Tommy Brock, first version, first and second variations

BP-2 Beswick Gold Oval

Between BP-2 and BP-3 there exist transitional backstamps. These appear on a very limited number of figures. The backstamp is part gold and part brown line; usually "Beatrix Potter" and the figure's name appear in gold with the last three lines in brown.

The following is a list of figures that can be found with the transitional backstamp:

Flopsy, Mopsy and Cottontail
Mr. Benjamin Bunny, first version
Mrs. Tittlemouse, style one
Peter Rabbit, first version, first variation
Squirrel Nutkin, first version, first variation
Timmy Tiptoes, first variation

Part gold, part brown line backstamp

BP-3   BESWICK BROWN LINE ISSUED 1973 TO 1988

There are three varieties of this backstamp, which has the words "Beswick" and "England" in a straight line. It was used on 70 figures plus 27 versions/varieties for 16 years.

BP-3a Potter's, no date, issued 1973 to 1974
(no copyright date)
Used on 41 figures, plus 9 versions/varieties

BP-3b Potter's, date, issued 1974 to 1985
(copyright date)
Used on 63 figures, plus 16 versions/varieties

BP-3c Potter, date, issued 1985 to 1988
(no "s" on Potter)
Used on 63 figures, plus 16 versions/varieties

BP-4   BESWICK SIGNATURE ISSUED 1988 TO 1989

This era saw the Beswick backstamp converted to the Royal Doulton backstamp. The connection with Beswick was kept by the addition of the John Beswick signature to the backstamp. In use for a year to a year and a half, this is one of the shortest time periods for a backstamp.

BP-4 Beswick Signature
Used on a total of 29 figures

BP-5   ROYAL ALBERT GOLD CROWN ISSUED 1989

The gold backstamp was reinstituted for 1989 to mark the change from the Doulton/Beswick backstamps to Royal Albert. It was used on only the following six figures:

Benjamin Bunny, third version, first variation
Flopsy, Mopsy and Cottontail
Hunca Munca
Jemima Puddleduck, first version, first variation
Mrs. Rabbit and Bunnies
Peter Rabbit, first version, second variation

BP-5 Royal Albert Gold Crown

BP-6 ROYAL ALBERT BROWN CROWN
ISSUED 1989 TO 1998

This backstamp was issued in two sizes. A small version was used on the standard figures with a larger size for the large size figures. The small size was issued in 1989 and was used on 90 figures. The large size was issued in 1993 and was used on 10 figures. A variation of the small size exists without the crown for small base figures.

BP-6a Small brown crown   **BP-6b** Large brown crown

BP-7 BESWICK BROWN OVAL
ISSUED 1993

Issued only on the large size Peter Rabbit to commemorate the 100th anniversary of Peter Rabbit 1893-1993.

BP-7 Brown Oval

BP-8 BESWICK WARE BROWN SCRIPT
ISSUED 1994 TO 1998

"Beswick Ware England" or the mark that followed, "Beswick Ware Made in England" is the earliest printed backstamp of the J. W. Beswick, Baltimore Works, Longton, and it was for the Beswick Centenary that the Beswick Ware logo was reinstated as the primary backstamp of the John Beswick Studio of Royal Doulton.

Since the first Beswick Ware stamp was used in 1894, and with the release of the new "Beswick Crest" series of backstamps in 1999, we find it now a good time put these backstamps in order.

BP-8a General Backstamp
Issued 1998

Issued as a general backstamp for a very short period of time in 1998, the brown script may turn out to be the rarest of the Beatrix Potter backstamps. It is found on only 2 figures.

Jemima and her Ducklings
Mrs. Tiggy-Winkle Washing

BP-8a Beswick Ware Brown Script

BP-8b 50th Anniversary of Production of
Beatrix Potter Figures at Beswick, Issued 1997

1997 was the 50th anniversary of production of Beatrix Potter figurines at the John Beswick Studios in Longton. This backstamp was in use only during 1997.

BP-8b Beswick 50th Anniversary

BP-8c Limited Edition Backstamp

BP-8c is a modification of BP-8a and designed for a limited edition figurines.

The following is a list of figures that can be found with a BP-8c backstamp:

Hiding From the Cat
Mittens, Tom Kitten and Moppet
Peter and Benjamin Picking Onions

BP-8c Beswick Ware Brown Script
Limited Edition Backstamp

BP-9   BESWICK WARE GOLD SCRIPT
ISSUED 1997 TO 1999

A gold Beswick Ware script backstamp was coupled with the anniversary, limited edition, gold or platinum highlighted figurines. There are three varieties of this backstamp.

BP-9a   100th Anniversary of
John Beswick Studios, Issued 1994

Issued to commemorate the 100th anniversary of the founding of the Beswick studios. This backstamp was available only on Jemima Puddle-Duck.

BP-9a Beswick Centenary

BP-9b   General Backstamp
1997-1998

The following small size figures issued with gold accents are coupled with gold Beswick Ware backstamps:

> Benjamin Bunny, third version, second variation
> Hunca Munca Sweeping, first version, second variation
> Jemima Puddle-Duck, first version, second variation
> Mrs. Tiggy-Winkle, first version, third variation
> Peter Rabbit, first version, third variation
> Tom Kitten, first version, third variation

BP-9b Beswick Gold Script

BP-9c   Limited Edition

This backstamp, a modification of BP-9b, appears on 12 large size figurines issued by Lawleys By Post between 1997-1999. They were issued and sold in pairs. A single double figure was issued in 2000.

> Benjamin Bunny, fourth version, second variation
> Peter Rabbit, second version, second variation
>
> Jemima Puddle-Duck, second version, second variation
> Mrs. Tiggy-Winkle, second version, second variation

Mr. Jeremy Fisher, second version, second variation
Tom Kitten, second version, second variation

Foxy Whiskered Gentleman, second version, second variation
Mrs. Rabbit, third version, second variation

Peter and the Red Pocket Handkerchief, second version, second variation
Tailor of Gloucester, second version, second variation

Hunca Munca Sweeping, second version
Squirrel Nutkin, second version

Mrs. Rabbit and Peter (Single issue-double figure)

Tabitha Twitchit and Moppet, second version

BP-9c Beswick Ware Gold Script
Limited Edition

BP-9d   Peter Rabbit and Friends
Limited Editions

This backstamp is a modification of BP-9b and is found on limited edition figures with gold accents issued by Peter Rabbit and Friends.

> Duchess and Ribby
> Ginger and Pickles
> Mrs. Tiggy-Winkle and Lucie
> Peter and the Red Pocket Handkerchief, first version, second variation
> This Pig Had a Bit of Meat

BP-9d Peter Rabbit and Friends
Limited Editions

BP-10
BESWICK BLACK CREST
ISSUED 1998 TO DATE

In 1998 the Beswick backstamp was redesigned and the Beswick crest, first seen in 1968-1969, was re-introduced for the Beswick line of Storybook figurines. There are three varieties of this backstamp.

BP-10a   Beswick Black Crest

This backstamp, now in general use, will be found on the following Beatrix Potter figurines:

Amiable Guinea-Pig, style two
And This Pig Had None
Appley Dapply, second version
Benjamin Ate a Lettuce Leaf
Farmer Potatoes
Foxy Whiskered Gentleman, first version
Hunca Munca Sweeping, first version
   first variation
Jemima and her Ducklings
Jemima Puddle-Duck, first version, first
   variation
Jemima Puddleduck with Foxy Whiskered
   Gentleman
Jeremy Fisher Catches a Fish
Johnny Town-Mouse Eating Corn
Lady Mouse
Mr. Jeremy Fisher, first version, second variation
Mrs. Tiggy-Winkle Takes Tea
Mrs. Tiggy-Winkle Washing
Mrs. Tittlemouse, style two
Old Mr. Brown
Peter and the Red Pocket Handkerchief,
   first version, first variation
Peter in Bed
Peter in the Watering Can
Squirrel Nutkin, first version, second variation
The Old Woman Who Lived in a Shoe Knitting
Timmy Willie Fetching Milk
Tom Kitten in the Rockery
Tommy Brock, second version, second variation
Yock-Yock in the Tub

BP-10a Beswick Black Crest

BP-10b   Beswick Black Arch

This backstamp is a modification of BP-10a and can be found on the following figurines. The modification was necessary due to base restriction.

Hunca Munca
Miss Moppet, second variation
Mr. Benjamin Bunny, second variation
Mr. Drake Puddle-Duck
Mr. McGregor
Mrs. Flopsy Bunny
Mrs. Rabbit and Peter, first version
Mrs. Rabbit Cooking

Peter Ate a Raddish
Peter Rabbit, first version, second variation
Peter Rabbit Gardening
Peter with Daffodils
Peter with Postbag
Rebeccah Puddle-Duck

BP-10b A modification of backstamp BP-10a

BP-10c   Beswick Black Circle

This backstamp is a modification of BP-10a. Its modification is also due to base restriction. It can be found on the following figurines:

Benjamin Bunny, third version, first variation
Little Pig Robinson, second variation
Mrs. Rabbit, second version
Mrs. Tiggy-Winkle, first version, second
   variation
Pigling Bland, second variation
Ribby
Tailor of Gloucester, first version
Tom Kitten, first version, second variation

BP-10c A modification of backstamp BP-10a

BP-11
BESWICK GOLD CREST
SPECIAL EDITIONS

At the time of publication BP-11 was found only on Sweet Peter Rabbit, a limited edition figurine commissioned by Peter Rabbit and Friends. This backstamp is a gold version of BP-10a

BP-11 Beswick Gold Crest

AMIABLE GUINEA-PIG™
Style One

Modeller:	Albert Hallam
Height:	3 ½", 8.9 cm
Colour:	Tan jacket, white waistcoat, yellow trousers
Issued:	1967 - 1983

Back Stamp	Beswick Number	Doulton Number	Price			
			U.S. $	Can. $	U.K. £	Aust. $
BP-2	2061	P2061	725.00	925.00	400.00	950.00
BP-3a			375.00	525.00	225.00	500.00
BP-3b			375.00	525.00	225.00	500.00

Note: The colour of the coat varies from tan to brown.

AMIABLE GUINEA-PIG™
Style Two

Modeller:	Warren Platt
Height:	4 ¼", 10.8 cm
Colour:	Brown jacket and waistcoat, beige trousers and hat, blue bowtie and book
Issued:	2000 to the present

Back Stamp	Beswick Number	Doulton Number	Price			
			U.S. $	Can. $	U.K. £	Aust. $
BP-10a	4031	P4031	48.00	—	28.00	—

AND THIS PIG HAD NONE™

Modeller:	Martyn Alcock
Height:	4", 10.1 cm
Colour:	Mauve dress, mottled burgundy and green shawl, brown hat
Issued:	1992 - 1998

Back Stamp	Beswick Number	Doulton Number	Price			
			U.S. $	Can. $	U.K. £	Aust. $
BP-6a	3319	P3319	55.00	75.00	25.00	85.00
BP-10a			45.00	65.00	20.00	70.00

ANNA MARIA™

Modeller: Albert Hallam
Height: 3", 7.6 cm
Colour: Blue dress and white apron
Issued: 1963 - 1983

Back Stamp	Beswick Number	Doulton Number	Price U.S. $	Can. $	U.K. £	Aust. $
BP-2	1851	P1851	525.00	650.00	300.00	525.00
BP-3a			250.00	300.00	135.00	275.00
BP-3b			250.00	300.00	135.00	275.00

Note: Dress is bright blue in earlier versions and pale blue in later versions.

First version: Bottle out

APPLEY DAPPLY™

Modeller: Albert Hallam
Height: 3 ¼", 8.3 cm
Colour: Brown mouse, white apron, blue trim, blue bow, yellow basket, tray of jam tarts

FIRST VERSION: BOTTLE OUT

Issued: 1971 - 1975

Back Stamp	Beswick Number	Doulton Number	Price U.S. $	Can. $	U.K. £	Aust. $
BP-2	2333/1	P2333/1	450.00	650.00	300.00	650.00
BP-3a			375.00	500.00	200.00	500.00
BP-3b			375.00	500.00	200.00	500.00

Second version: Bottle in

SECOND VERSION: BOTTLE IN

Issued: 1975 to the present

Back Stamp	Beswick Number	Doulton Number	Price U.S. $	Can. $	U.K. £	Aust. $
BP-3b	2333/2	P2333/2	85.00	115.00	50.00	115.00
BP-3c			95.00	130.00	60.00	130.00
BP-6a			35.00	50.00	20.00	50.00
BP-10a			36.00	63.00	17.50	70.00

AUNT PETTITOES™

Modeller:	Albert Hallam
Height:	3 ¾", 9.5 cm
Colour:	Blue dress and white cap with blue polka dots
Issued:	1970 - 1993

Back Stamp	Beswick Number	Doulton Number	Price			
			U.S. $	Can. $	U.K. £	Aust. $
BP-2	2276	P2276	600.00	675.00	300.00	700.00
BP-3a			95.00	135.00	65.00	150.00
BP-3b			75.00	95.00	50.00	100.00
BP-3c			85.00	125.00	55.00	125.00
BP-6a			90.00	125.00	60.00	125.00

Note: The dress is light blue in earlier versions and bright blue in later versions.

BABBITTY BUMBLE™

Modeller:	Warren Platt
Height:	2 ¾", 7.0 cm
Colour:	Black and gold
Issued:	1989 - 1993

Back Stamp	Beswick Number	Doulton Number	Price			
			U.S. $	Can. $	U.K. £	Aust. $
BP-6a	2971	P2971	275.00	375.00	175.00	375.00

BENJAMIN ATE A LETTUCE LEAF™

Modeller:	Martyn Alcock
Height:	4 ¾", 11.9 cm
Colour:	Brown, white and yellow
Issued:	1992 - 1998

Back Stamp	Beswick Number	Doulton Number	Price			
			U.S. $	Can. $	U.K. £	Aust. $
BP-6a	3317	P3317	50.00	65.00	22.00	75.00
BP-10a			45.00	65.00	18.00	75.00

First version: Ears out, shoes out

Second version: Ears out, shoes in

Third version: Ears in, shoes in

BENJAMIN BUNNY™

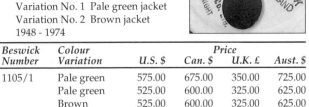

Modeller:	Arthur Gredington
Height:	4", 10.1 cm
Size:	Small

FIRST VERSION: EARS OUT, SHOES OUT

Colour:	Variation No. 1 Pale green jacket
	Variation No. 2 Brown jacket
Issued:	1948 - 1974

Back Stamp	Beswick Number	Colour Variation	U.S. $	Can. $	U.K. £	Aust. $
BP-1a	1105/1	Pale green	575.00	675.00	350.00	725.00
BP-2		Pale green	525.00	600.00	325.00	625.00
BP-2		Brown	525.00	600.00	325.00	625.00
BP-3a		Pale green	400.00	500.00	275.00	450.00
BP-3b		Brown	350.00	450.00	250.00	425.00

SECOND VERSION: EARS OUT, SHOES IN

Colour:	Variation No. 1 Pale green jacket
	Variation No. 2 Brown jacket
Issued:	1972 - c.1980

Back Stamp	Beswick Number	Colour Variation	U.S. $	Can. $	U.K. £	Aust. $
BP-2	1105/2	Pale green	500.00	575.00	300.00	550.00
BP-3a		Pale green	350.00	375.00	250.00	375.00
BP-3a		Brown	350.00	375.00	250.00	375.00
BP-3b		Pale green	300.00	325.00	225.00	325.00
BP-3b		Brown	300.00	325.00	225.00	325.00

THIRD VERSION: EARS IN, SHOES IN
FIRST VARIATION: BROWN SHOES

Colour:	Brown jacket, green beret with orange pompon
Issued:	c.1980 - 2000

Back Stamp	Beswick Number	Doulton Number	U.S. $	Can. $	U.K. £	Aust. $
BP-3b	1105/3	P1105/3	95.00	125.00	60.00	135.00
BP-3c			95.00	125.00	60.00	135.00
BP-4			100.00	135.00	70.00	150.00
BP-5			150.00	200.00	90.00	200.00
BP-6a			35.00	60.00	22.00	70.00
BP-10c			36.00	65.00	17.00	70.00

THIRD VERSION: EARS IN, SHOES IN
SECOND VARIATION: GOLD SHOES

Colour:	Brown jacket, green beret with orange pompon, gold shoes
Issued:	1998 - 1998

Back Stamp	Beswick Number	Doulton Number	U.S. $	Can. $	U.K. £	Aust. $
BP-9b	1105/4	PG1105	60.00	80.00	30.00	100.00

BENJAMIN BUNNY™

Modeller: Martyn Alcock
Height: 6 ¼", 15.9 cm
Size: Large

FOURTH VERSION: LARGE SIZE, EARS IN, SHOES IN
FIRST VARIATION: BROWN SHOES

Colour: Tan jacket, green beret with orange pompon
Issued: 1994 - 1997

Back Stamp	Beswick Number	Doulton Number	Price			
			U.S. $	Can. $	U.K. £	Aust. $
BP-6b	3403/1	P3403	60.00	95.00	40.00	100.00

FOURTH VERSION: LARGE SIZE, EARS IN, SHOES IN
SECOND VARIATION, GOLD SHOES

Issued: 1997 in a limited edition of 1,947
Series: Gold edition

Back Stamp	Beswick Number	Doulton Number	Price			
			U.S. $	Can. $	U.K. £	Aust. $
BP-9c	3403/2	PG3403	60.00	95.00	40.00	100.00

Note: Issued, numbered and sold as a pair with Peter Rabbit, second version, second variation.

Benjamin Bunny, large size

BENJAMIN BUNNY SAT ON A BANK™

Modeller: David Lyttleton
Height: 3 ¾", 9.5 cm

FIRST VERSION: HEAD LOOKS DOWN

Colour: Brown jacket
Issued: 1983 - 1985

BEATRIX POTTER'S
"Benjamin Bunny"
"Sat on a bank"
© Frederick Warne P.L.C. 1983
BESWICK ENGLAND

Back Stamp	Beswick Number	Doulton Number	Price			
			U.S. $	Can. $	U.K. £	Aust. $
BP-3b	2803/1	P2803/1	125.00	150.00	75.00	150.00
BP-3c			150.00	175.00	100.00	175.00

First version: Head looks down

BEATRIX POTTER'S
"Benjamin Bunny"
"Sat on a bank"
© Frederick Warne P.L.C. 1983
BESWICK ENGLAND

SECOND VERSION: HEAD LOOKS UP

Colour: Golden brown jacket
Issued: 1983 - 1997

Back Stamp	Beswick Number	Doulton Number	Price			
			U.S. $	Can. $	U.K. £	Aust. $
BP-3b	2803/2	P2803/2	125.00	165.00	90.00	165.00
BP-3c			150.00	185.00	100.00	190.00
BP-6a			50.00	65.00	30.00	70.00

Second version: Head looks up

BENJAMIN WAKES UP™

Modeller:	Amanda Hughes-Lubeck	
Height:	2 ¼", 5.7 cm	
Colour:	Green, white and orange	
Issued:	1991 - 1997	

Back Stamp	Beswick Number	Doulton Number	U.S. $	Can. $	U.K. £	Aust. $
					Price	
BP-6a	3234	P3234	50.00	75.00	25.00	80.00

First version: Head down

CECILY PARSLEY™

Modeller:	Arthur Gredington
Height:	4", 10.1 cm

FIRST VERSION: HEAD DOWN, BRIGHT BLUE DRESS

Colour:	Bright blue dress, white apron, brown pail
Issued:	1965 - 1985

Back Stamp	Beswick Number	Doulton Number	U.S. $	Can. $	U.K. £	Aust. $
					Price	
BP-2	1941/1	P1941/1	300.00	400.00	175.00	375.00
BP-3a			120.00	150.00	75.00	175.00
BP-3b			95.00	120.00	60.00	135.00
BP-3c			100.00	135.00	65.00	135.00

Second version: Head up

SECOND VERSION: HEAD UP, PALE BLUE DRESS

Colour:	Pale blue dress, white apron
Issued:	1985 - 1993

Back Stamp	Beswick Number	Doulton Number	U.S. $	Can. $	U.K. £	Aust. $
					Price	
BP-3c	1941/2	P1941/2	125.00	150.00	75.00	160.00
BP-6a			60.00	90.00	40.00	95.00

Note: Cecily Parsley was issued with both a dark and a light blue dress.

CHIPPY HACKEE™

Modeller:	David Lyttleton
Height:	3 ¾", 9.5 cm
Colour:	Pale green blanket, white handkerchief, green foot bath
Issued:	1979 - 1993

Back Stamp	Beswick Number	Doulton Number	Price U.S. $	Can. $	U.K. £	Aust. $
BP-3b	2627	P2627	90.00	125.00	60.00	125.00
BP-3c			110.00	150.00	70.00	150.00
BP-6a			75.00	100.00	45.00	100.00

Note: The colour of the blanket may range from pale green to pale yellow.

CHRISTMAS STOCKING™

Modeller:	Martyn Alcock
Height:	3 ¼", 8.3 cm
Colour:	Brown mice, red and white striped stocking
Issued:	1991 - 1994

Back Stamp	Beswick Number	Doulton Number	Price U.S. $	Can. $	U.K. £	Aust. $
BP-6a	3257	P3257	275.00	350.00	175.00	375.00

COTTONTAIL™

Modeller:	David Lyttleton
Height:	3 ¾", 9.5 cm
Colour:	Blue dress, brown chair
Issued:	1985 - 1996

Back Stamp	Beswick Number	Doulton Number	Price U.S. $	Can. $	U.K. £	Aust. $
BP-3b	2878	P2878	75.00	90.00	50.00	90.00
BP-3c			85.00	110.00	55.00	110.00
BP-4			90.00	125.00	60.00	125.00
BP-6a			60.00	75.00	30.00	75.00

COUSIN RIBBY™

Modeller:	Albert Hallam
Height:	3 ½", 8.9 cm
Colour:	Pink skirt and hat, green apron, blue shawl, yellow basket
Issued:	1970 - 1993

Back Stamp	Beswick Number	Doulton Number	Price			
			U.S. $	Can. $	U.K. £	Aust. $
BP-2	2284	P2284	600.00	675.00	350.00	700.00
BP-3a			75.00	100.00	50.00	90.00
BP-3b			75.00	100.00	50.00	90.00
BP-3c			75.00	100.00	50.00	90.00
BP-6a			80.00	110.00	60.00	110.00

BEATRIX POTTER'S
Cousin Ribby
F. WARNE & CO. LTD.
COPYRIGHT
BESWICK
ENGLAND

DIGGORY DIGGORY DELVET™

Modeller:	David Lyttleton
Height:	2 ¾", 7.0 cm
Colour:	Grey mole
Issued:	1982 - 1997

Back Stamp	Beswick Number	Doulton Number	Price			
			U.S. $	Can. $	U.K. £	Aust. $
BP-3b	2713	P2713	75.00	110.00	50.00	125.00
BP-3c			75.00	110.00	50.00	125.00
BP-6a			50.00	75.00	30.00	75.00

BEATRIX POTTER
"Diggory Diggory Delvet"
© Frederick Warne & Co. 1982
Licensed by Copyrights
BESWICK ENGLAND

DUCHESS™
Style One (Holding Flowers)

Modeller:	Graham Orwell
Height:	3 ¾", 9.5 cm
Colour:	Black dog, multicoloured flowers
Issued:	1955 - 1967

BEATRIX POTTER
DUCHESS
WARNE & CO. L⁴
BESWICK
ENGLAND

Back Stamp	Beswick Number	Doulton Number	Price			
			U.S. $	Can. $	U.K. £	Aust. $
BP-1	1355	P1355		Extremely	Rare	
BP-2			3,000.00	4,500.00	1,800.00	4,500.00

Note: Italicized prices are indications only, and the actual selling price may be higher or lower, depending on market conditions.

DUCHESS™
Style Two (Holding a Pie)

Modeller:	Graham Tongue
Height:	4", 10.1 cm
Colour:	Black dog, blue bow, light brown pie
Issued:	1979 - 1982

Back Stamp	Beswick Number	Doulton Number	Price			
			U.S. $	Can. $	U.K. £	Aust. $
BP-3b	2601	P2601	500.00	600.00	275.00	600.00

FARMER POTATOES™

Modeller:	Shane Ridge
Height:	5", 12.7 cm
Colour:	Tan jacket, brown trousers, yellow shirt, blue hat and lantern
Issued:	2000 to the present

Back Stamp	Beswick Number	Doulton Number	Price			
			U.S. $	Can. $	U.K. £	Aust. $
BP-10a	4014	P4014	60.00	—	32.00	—

First version: Feet out

FIERCE BAD RABBIT™

Modeller: David Lyttleton
Height: 4 ¾", 12.1 cm

FIRST VERSION: FEET OUT

Colour: Dark brown and white rabbit,
         red-brown carrot, green seat
Issued: 1977 - 1980

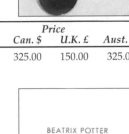

Back	Beswick	Doulton	Price			
Stamp	Number	Number	U.S. $	Can. $	U.K. £	Aust. $
BP-3b	2586/1	P2586/1	225.00	325.00	150.00	325.00

SECOND VERSION: FEET IN

Colour: Light brown and white rabbit,
         red-brown carrot, green seat
Issued: 1980 - 1997

Back	Beswick	Doulton	Price			
Stamp	Number	Number	U.S. $	Can. $	U.K. £	Aust. $
BP-3b	2586/2	P2586/2	100.00	125.00	65.00	150.00
BP-3c			100.00	125.00	65.00	150.00
BP-4			100.00	125.00	65.00	150.00
BP-6a			55.00	75.00	30.00	85.00

Second version: Feet in

FLOPSY, MOPSY AND COTTONTAIL™

Modeller: Arthur Gredington
Height: 2 ½", 6.4 cm
Colour: Brown and white rabbits
           wearing rose-pink cloaks
Issued: 1954 - 1997

Back	Beswick	Doulton	Price			
Stamp	Number	Number	U.S. $	Can. $	U.K. £	Aust. $
BP-1a	1274	P1274	450.00	550.00	300.00	525.00
BP-2			300.00	350.00	175.00	325.00
BP-3a			95.00	125.00	60.00	100.00
BP-3b			95.00	125.00	60.00	100.00
BP-3c			95.00	125.00	60.00	100.00
BP-4			100.00	125.00	65.00	125.00
BP-5			200.00	275.00	125.00	250.00
BP-6a			55.00	75.00	30.00	75.00

Note: Colour variations of the cloaks exist. Angle of bunnies heads may vary.

FOXY READING COUNTRY NEWS™

Modeller: Amanda Hughes-Lubeck
Height: 4 ¼", 10.8 cm
Colour: Brown and green
Issued: 1990 - 1997

Back Stamp	Beswick Number	Doulton Number	Price			
			U.S. $	Can. $	U.K. £	Aust. $
BP-6a	3219	P3219	75.00	100.00	40.00	100.00

FOXY WHISKERED GENTLEMAN™

Modeller: Arthur Gredington

FIRST VERSION: SMALL

Height: 4 ¾", 12.1 cm
Size: Small
Colour: Pale green jacket and trousers, pink waistcoat
Issued: 1954 to the present

Back Stamp	Beswick Number	Doulton Number	Price			
			U.S. $	Can. $	U.K. £	Aust. $
BP-1a	1277	P1277	450.00	525.00	300.00	525.00
BP-2			300.00	350.00	125.00	375.00
BP-3a			125.00	150.00	75.00	165.00
BP-3b			90.00	125.00	55.00	125.00
BP-3c			100.00	150.00	60.00	150.00
BP-4			125.00	175.00	60.00	175.00
BP-6a			60.00	75.00	30.00	75.00
BP-10a			36.00	—	17.50	—

Note: Variations occur with the head looking either right or left.

Small size

SECOND VERSION: LARGE
FIRST VARIATION: GREEN BUTTONS

Height: 7 ½", 19.1 cm
Size: Large
Colour: Pale green jacket and trousers, pink waistcoat
Issued: 1995 - 1997

Back Stamp	Beswick Number	Doulton Number	Price			
			U.S. $	Can. $	U.K. £	Aust. $
BP-6b	3450/1	P3450	65.00	95.00	35.00	90.00

SECOND VERSION: LARGE
SECOND VARIATION: GOLD BUTTONS

Height: 7 ½", 19.1 cm
Size: Large
Colour: Pale green jacket and trousers, pink waistcoat, gold buttons
Issued: 1998 in a limited edition of 1,947
Series: Gold edition

Back Stamp	Beswick Number	Doulton Number	Price			
			U.S. $	Can. $	U.K. £	Aust. $
BP-9c	3450/2	PG3450	80.00	95.00	40.00	100.00

Note: The gold edition was issued, numbered and sold as a pair with Mrs. Rabbit, third version, first variation.

Large size

GENTLEMAN MOUSE MADE A BOW™

Modeller:	Ted Chawner
Height:	3", 7.6 cm
Colour:	Brown, blue and white
Issued:	1990 - 1996

Back Stamp	Beswick Number	Doulton Number	Price			
			U.S. $	Can. $	U.K. £	Aust. $
BP-6a	3200	P3200	75.00	110.00	40.00	110.00

GINGER™

Modeller:	David Lyttleton
Height:	3 ¾", 9.5 cm
Colour:	Green, white and brown
Issued:	1976 - 1982

Back Stamp	Beswick Number	Doulton Number	Price			
			U.S. $	Can. $	U.K. £	Aust. $
BP-3b	2559	P2559	675.00	875.00	400.00	925.00

Note: The jacket colour varies from light to dark green.

GOODY TIPTOES™

Modeller:	Arthur Gredington
Height:	3 ½", 8.9 cm
Colour:	Grey squirrel wearing pink dress and white apron, brown sack with yellow nuts
Issued:	1961 - 1997

Back Stamp	Beswick Number	Doulton Number	Price			
			U.S. $	Can. $	U.K. £	Aust. $
BP-2	1675	P1675	300.00	375.00	200.00	375.00
BP-3a			100.00	125.00	60.00	125.00
BP-3b			75.00	100.00	45.00	100.00
BP-3c			100.00	125.00	60.00	125.00
BP-6a			55.00	75.00	30.00	85.00

Note: This model has two different bases and the dress comes in various shades of pink.

GOODY AND TIMMY TIPTOES™

Modeller: David Lyttleton
Height: 4", 10.1 cm
Colour: Timmy - rose coat
Goody - pink overdress with
green and biege underskirt,
green umbrella
Issued: 1986 - 1996

BEATRIX POTTER
"Goody & Timmy Tiptoes"
© Frederick Warne & Co. 1986
Licensed by Copyrights
BESWICK ENGLAND

Back Stamp	Beswick Number	Doulton Number	Price			
			U.S. $	Can. $	U.K. £	Aust. $
BP-3c	2957	P2957	300.00	425.00	200.00	400.00
BP-6a			100.00	100.00	60.00	95.00

HUNCA MUNCA™

Modeller: Arthur Gredington
Height: 2 ¾", 7.0 cm
Colour: Blue dress, white apron,
pink blanket and straw cradle
Issued: 1951 - 2000

BEATRIX POTTER'S
"HUNCA MUNCA"
F. WARNE & Co. LTD,
COPYRIGHT

Back Stamp	Beswick Number	Doulton Number	Price			
			U.S. $	Can. $	U.K. £	Aust. $
BP-1a	1198	P1198	350.00	375.00	200.00	325.00
BP-2			250.00	275.00	165.00	250.00
BP-3a			90.00	125.00	50.00	100.00
BP-3b			75.00	100.00	40.00	90.00
BP-3c			85.00	115.00	45.00	95.00
BP-4			100.00	135.00	75.00	110.00
BP-5			125.00	175.00	80.00	150.00
BP-6a			55.00	75.00	30.00	75.00
BP-10b			36.00	65.00	17.00	70.00

HUNCA MUNCA SPILLS THE BEADS™
First Version

Modeller: Martyn Alcock
Height: 3 ¼", 8.3 cm
Colour: Brown mouse, blue and
white rice jar
Issued: 1992 - 1996

ROYAL ALBERT ®
ENGLAND
Hunca Munca
spills the beads
Beatrix Potter
© F WARNE & CO 1991
© 1992 ROYAL ALBERT LTD

Back Stamp	Beswick Number	Doulton Number	Price			
			U.S. $	Can. $	U.K. £	Aust. $
BP-6a	3288	P3288	70.00	90.00	40.00	95.00

Green broom handle

Gold dustpan

Gold dustpan and broom handle

HUNCA MUNCA SWEEPING™

Modeller:	David Lyttleton
Height:	3 ½", 8.9 cm
Size:	Small

FIRST VERSION: SMALL SIZE
FIRST VARIATION: LIGHT BROWN
DUSTPAN

Colour:	Mauve patterned dress with white apron, green broom handle
Issued:	1977 to the present

BEATRIX POTTER'S
"Hunca Munca Sweeping"
F. Warne & Co.Ltd.
© Copyright 1977
BESWICK ENGLAND

Back Stamp	Beswick Number	Doulton Number	Price			
			U.S. $	Can. $	U.K. £	Aust. $
BP-3b	2584/1	P2584	95.00	125.00	60.00	125.00
BP-3c			100.00	135.00	65.00	140.00
BP-4			100.00	150.00	65.00	160.00
BP-6a			35.00	50.00	20.00	65.00
BP-10a			36.00	—	17.50	—

FIRST VERSION: SMALL SIZE
SECOND VARIATION: GOLD DUSTPAN

Colour:	Mauve patterned dress, white apron, green broom handle, gold dustpan
Issued:	1998 - 1998

Back Stamp	Beswick Number	Doulton Number	Price			
			U.S. $	Can. $	U.K. £	Aust. $
BP-9b	2584/2	PG2584	70.00	85.00	30.00	90.00

SECOND VERSION: LARGE SIZE, GOLD DUSTPAN

Modeller:	Amanda Hughes-Lubeck
Height:	5 ¼", 13.3 cm
Size:	Large
Colour:	Mauve patterned dress, white apron, gold dustpan and broom handle
Issued:	1999 in a limited edition of 1,947
Series:	Gold edition

Back Stamp	Beswick Number	Doulton Number	Price			
			U.S. $	Can. $	U.K. £	Aust. $
BP-9c	3894	PG3894	75.00	95.00	40.00	100.00

Note: Issued, numbered and sold as a pair with Squirrel Nutkin, large size.

JEMIMA AND HER DUCKLINGS™

Modeller: Martyn Alcock
Height: 4 ¼", 10.5 cm
Colour: Mauve shawl
Issued: 1998 to the present

Back Stamp	Beswick Number	Doulton Number	Price			
			U.S. $	Can. $	U.K. £	Aust. $
BP-8a	3786	P3786	Rare			
BP-10a			60.00	110.00	29.00	100.00

Note: Very few examples of BP-8a are known.

JEMIMA PUDDLE-DUCK™

Modeller: Arthur Gredington
Height: 4 ¾", 12.1 cm
Size: Small

FIRST VERSION: SMALL SIZE
FIRST VARIATION: YELLOW SCARF CLIP

Colour: Mauve or pink shawl, light blue bonnet, yellow scarf clip
Issued: 1948 to the present

Back Stamp	Beswick Number	Doulton Number	Price			
			U.S. $	Can. $	U.K. £	Aust. $
BP-1a	1092/1	P1092	275.00	350.00	175.00	375.00
BP-2			175.00	225.00	100.00	250.00
BP-3a			90.00	125.00	60.00	125.00
BP-3b			90.00	125.00	60.00	125.00
BP-3c			75.00	100.00	50.00	110.00
BP-4			95.00	125.00	60.00	135.00
BP-5			125.00	165.00	90.00	175.00
BP-6a			60.00	80.00	25.00	85.00
BP-10a			36.00	—	17.00	—

Small size, yellow scarf clip

FIRST VERSION: SMALL SIZE
SECOND VARIATION: GOLD SCARF CLIP

Colour: Mauve or pink shawl, light blue bonnet, gold scarf clip
Issued: 1997 - 1997

Back Stamp	Beswick Number	Doulton Number	Price			
			U.S. $	Can. $	U.K. £	Aust. $
BP-9b	1092/2	PG1092	50.00	75.00	30.00	85.00

Small size, gold scarf clip

Large size, yellow scarf clip

Large size, gold scarf clip

JEMIMA PUDDLE-DUCK™

Modeller:	Martyn Alcock
Height:	6", 15.0 cm
Size:	Large

Beswick Ware
MADE IN ENGLAND
BEATRIX POTTER'S
JEMIMA PUDDLE-DUCK
BESWICK CENTENARY
1894–1994
© F. WARNE & CO. 1993
© 1993 ROYAL DOULTON

SECOND VERSION: LARGE SIZE
FIRST VARIATION: YELLOW SCARF CLIP

Colour:	White duck, mauve shawl, light blue bonnet, yellow scarf clip
Issued:	1993 - 1997

Back Stamp	Beswick Number	Doulton Number	Price U.S. $	Can. $	U.K. £	Aust. $
BP-6b	3373/1	P3373	75.00	100.00	40.00	125.00
BP-9a	Beswick Centenary		100.00	125.00	50.00	125.00

SECOND VERSION: LARGE SIZE
SECOND VARIATION: GOLD SCARF CLIP

Colour:	White duck, mauve shawl, light blue bonnet, gold scarf clip
Issued:	1998 in a limited edition of 1,947
Series:	Gold edition

Back Stamp	Beswick Number	Doulton Number	Price U.S. $	Can. $	U.K. £	Aust. $
BP-9c	3373/2	PG3373	75.00	100.00	40.00	100.00

Note: The second variation was issued, numbered and sold as a pair with Mrs. Tiggy-Winkle, second version, second variation.

JEMIMA PUDDLE-DUCK MADE A FEATHER NEST™

Modeller:	David Lyttleton
Height:	2 ¼", 5.7 cm
Colour:	White duck, mauve or pink shawl, blue hat
Issued:	1983 - 1997

BEATRIX POTTER'S
Jemima Puddleduck
Made a feather nest
© Frederick Warne P.L.C. 1983
BESWICK
ENGLAND

Back Stamp	Beswick Number	Doulton Number	Price U.S. $	Can. $	U.K. £	Aust. $
BP-3b	2823	P2823	75.00	90.00	45.00	95.00
BP-3c			75.00	90.00	45.00	95.00
BP-4			100.00	115.00	55.00	125.00
BP-6a			50.00	75.00	30.00	75.00

Note: This model was issued with either a mauve or pink shawl.

JEMIMA PUDDLE-DUCK WITH FOXY WHISKERED GENTLEMAN™

Modeller:	Ted Chawner	
Height:	4 ¾", 12.1 cm	
Colour:	Brown, green, white and blue	
Issued:	1990 - 1999	

Back Stamp	Beswick Number	Doulton Number	Price U.S. $	Can. $	U.K. £	Aust. $
BP-6a	3193	P3193	100.00	125.00	50.00	125.00
BP-10a			90.00	115.00	40.00	115.00

JEREMY FISHER CATCHES A FISH™

Modeller:	Martyn Alcock	
Height:	3", 7.6 cm	
Colour:	Green frog with brown spots, lilac coat, green, yellow and red fish	
Issued:	1999 to the present	

Back Stamp	Beswick Number	Doulton Number	Price U.S. $	Can. $	U.K. £	Aust. $
BP-10a	3919	P3919	60.00	135.00	36.00	—

Note: There are two variations of P3919: the base can be found with a cut-out "v" through both the lilypad and the water, and with a half-way "v" through the lilypad but not through the water (as illustrated).

JOHN JOINER™

Modeller:	Graham Tongue	
Height:	2 ½", 6.4 cm	
Colour:	Brown dog wearing green jacket	
Issued:	1990 - 1997	

Back Stamp	Beswick Number	Doulton Number	Price U.S. $	Can. $	U.K. £	Aust. $
BP-6a	2965	P2965	65.00	90.00	40.00	95.00

Note: John Joiner will vary in shade from black to blue-black.

JOHNNY TOWN-MOUSE™

Modeller: Arthur Gredington
Height: 3 ½", 8.9 cm
Colour: Pale blue jacket, white and brown waistcoat
Issued: 1954 - 1993

Back Stamp	Beswick Number	Doulton Number	Price			
			U.S. $	Can. $	U.K. £	Aust. $
BP-1a	1276	P1276	300.00	400.00	200.00	425.00
BP-2			200.00	250.00	125.00	275.00
BP-3a			90.00	125.00	60.00	125.00
BP-3b			90.00	125.00	60.00	125.00
BP-3c			90.00	125.00	60.00	125.00
BP-6a			60.00	85.00	35.00	95.00

Note: Jacket colouring varies from pale to deep blue.

JOHNNY TOWN-MOUSE EATING CORN™

Modeller: Martyn Alcock
Height: 3 ¾", 9.5 cm
Colour: Blue jacket, green and white waistcoat, pink trousers
Issued: 2000 to the present

Back Stamp	Beswick Number	Doulton Number	Price			
			U.S. $	Can. $	U.K. £	Aust. $
BP-10a	3931	P3931	48.00	90.00	25.00	—

JOHNNY TOWN-MOUSE WITH BAG™

Modeller: Ted Chawner
Height: 3 ½", 8.9 cm
Colour: Light brown coat and hat, yellow-cream waistcoat
Issued: 1988 - 1994

Back Stamp	Beswick Number	Doulton Number	Price			
			U.S. $	Can. $	U.K. £	Aust. $
BP-4	3094	P3094	350.00	425.00	200.00	450.00
BP-6a			150.00	200.00	100.00	200.00

LADY MOUSE™

Modeller:	Arthur Gredington		
Height:	4", 10.1 cm		
Colour:	White dress with yellow trim and blue polka-dot sleeves, white hat with purple and blue highlights		
Issued:	1950 - 2000		

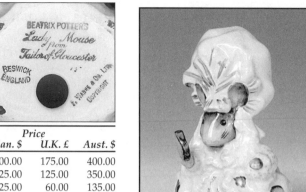

Back Stamp	Beswick Number	Doulton Number	U.S. $	Can. $	U.K. £	Aust. $
				Price		
BP-1a	1183	P1183	325.00	400.00	175.00	400.00
BP-2			225.00	325.00	125.00	350.00
BP-3a			100.00	125.00	60.00	135.00
BP-3b			85.00	100.00	60.00	115.00
BP-3c			100.00	125.00	60.00	135.00
BP-6a			50.00	75.00	30.00	75.00
BP-10a			36.00	65.00	18.00	75.00

LADY MOUSE MADE A CURTSY™

Modeller:	Amanda Hughes-Lubeck
Height:	3 ¼", 8.3 cm
Colour:	Purple-pink and white
Issued:	1990 - 1997

Back Stamp	Beswick Number	Doulton Number	U.S. $	Can. $	U.K. £	Aust. $
				Price		
BP-6a	3220	P3220	50.00	75.00	30.00	80.00

LITTLE BLACK RABBIT™

Modeller:	David Lyttleton
Height:	4 ½", 11.4 cm
Colour:	Black rabbit wearing green waistcoat
Issued:	1977 - 1997

Back Stamp	Beswick Number	Doulton Number	U.S. $	Can. $	U.K. £	Aust. $
				Price		
BP-3b	2585	P2585	75.00	100.00	50.00	85.00
BP-3c			75.00	100.00	50.00	85.00
BP-4			125.00	175.00	75.00	150.00
BP-6a			55.00	75.00	35.00	80.00

Note: The jacket colouring varies from light to dark green.

First version: Blue striped outfit

Second version: Blue checked outfit

LITTLE PIG ROBINSON™

Modeller: Arthur Gredington

FIRST VARIATION: BLUE STRIPED OUTFIT

Height: 4", 10.2 cm
Colour: White and blue striped
          outfit, brown basket
          with yellow cauliflowers
Issued: 1948 - 1974

Back Stamp	Beswick Number	Doulton Number	U.S. $	Can. $	U.K. £	Aust. $
BP-1a	1104/1	P1104/1	475.00	675.00	300.00	650.00
BP-2			375.00	475.00	200.00	475.00
BP-3a			275.00	400.00	150.00	425.00
BP-3b			275.00	400.00	150.00	425.00

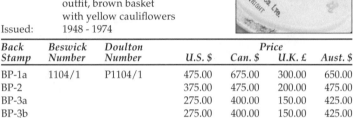

SECOND VARIATION: BLUE CHECKED OUTFIT

Height: 3 ½", 8.9 cm
Colour: Blue outfit, brown basket
          with cream cauliflowers
Issued: c.1974 - 1999

Back Stamp	Beswick Number	Doulton Number	U.S. $	Can. $	U.K. £	Aust. $
BP-3b	1104/2	P1104/2	80.00	100.00	50.00	110.00
BP-3c			75.00	100.00	45.00	110.00
BP-6a			55.00	75.00	30.00	75.00
BP-10c			40.00	65.00	20.00	75.00

LITTLE PIG ROBINSON SPYING™

Modeller: Ted Chawner
Height: 3 ½", 8.9 cm
Colour: Blue and white striped
           outfit, rose-pink chair
Issued: 1987 - 1993

Back Stamp	Beswick Number	Doulton Number	U.S. $	Can. $	U.K. £	Aust. $
BP-3c	3031	P3031	275.00	325.00	150.00	350.00
BP-6a			150.00	200.00	100.00	200.00

MISS DORMOUSE™

Modeller:	Martyn Alcock
Height:	4", 10.1 cm
Colour:	Blue, white and pink
Issued:	1991 - 1995

Back Stamp	Beswick Number	Doulton Number	Price			
			U.S. $	Can. $	U.K. £	Aust. $
BP-6a	3251	P3251	100.00	150.00	60.00	165.00

MISS MOPPET™

Modeller:	Arthur Gredington
Height:	3", 7.6 cm

FIRST VARIATION: MOTTLED BROWN CAT

Colour:	Mottled brown cat, blue checkered kerchief
Issued:	1954 - c.1978

Back Stamp	Beswick Number	Doulton Number	Price			
			U.S. $	Can. $	U.K. £	Aust. $
BP-1a	1275/1	P1275/1	250.00	350.00	150.00	375.00
BP-2			200.00	300.00	125.00	325.00
BP-3a			165.00	225.00	95.00	250.00
BP-3b			165.00	225.00	95.00	250.00

First version: Mottled brown cat

SECOND VARIATION: BROWN STRIPED CAT

Colour:	Striped brown cat, blue checkered kerchief
Issued:	1978 to the present

Back Stamp	Beswick Number	Doulton Number	Price			
			U.S. $	Can. $	U.K. £	Aust. $
BP3a	1275/2	P1275/2	85.00	115.00	50.00	125.00
BP-3b			75.00	110.00	50.00	115.00
BP-3c			65.00	100.00	45.00	110.00
BP-6a			40.00	55.00	25.00	70.00
BP-10b			36.00	—	17.50	—

Second version: Brown striped cat

MITTENS AND MOPPET™

Modeller:	Ted Chawner	
Height:	3 ¾", 9.5 cm	
Colour:	Blue, brown and grey	
Issued:	1990 - 1994	

Back Stamp	Beswick Number	Doulton Number	Price			
			U.S. $	Can. $	U.K. £	Aust. $
BP-6a	3197	P3197	250.00	325.00	125.00	350.00

MOTHER LADYBIRD™

Modeller:	Warren Platt	
Height:	2 ½", 6.4 cm	
Colour:	Red and black	
Issued:	1989 - 1996	

Back Stamp	Beswick Number	Doulton Number	Price			
			U.S. $	Can. $	U.K. £	Aust. $
BP-6a	2966	P2966	95.00	125.00	50.00	125.00

MR. ALDERMAN PTOLEMY™

Modeller:	Graham Tongue	
Height:	3 ½", 8.9 cm	
Colour:	Brown, grey and green	
Issued:	1973 - 1997	

Back Stamp	Beswick Number	Doulton Number	Price			
			U.S. $	Can. $	U.K. £	Aust. $
BP-3a	2424	P2424	200.00	275.00	125.00	250.00
BP-3b			175.00	225.00	110.00	225.00
BP-3c			175.00	250.00	100.00	250.00
BP-6a			60.00	80.00	35.00	85.00

MR. BENJAMIN BUNNY™

Modeller: Arthur Gredington
Height: 4 ¼", 10.8 cm

FIRST VERSION: PIPE OUT

Colour: Variation No. 1 Dark maroon jacket
Variation No. 2 Lilac jacket
Issued: 1965 - 1974

Back Stamp	Beswick Number	Colour Variation	Price			
			U.S. $	Can. $	U.K. £	Aust. $
BP-2	1940/1	Dark maroon	550.00	800.00	325.00	750.00
BP-3a		Dark maroon	475.00	625.00	275.00	625.00
BP-3a		Lilac	475.00	625.00	275.00	625.00

First version: Pipe out

SECOND VERSION: PIPE IN

Colour: Variation No. 1 Dark maroon jacket
Variation No. 2 Lilac jacket
Issued: 1. c.1970 - c.1974
2. 1975 - 2000

Back Stamp	Beswick Number	Colour Variation	Price			
			U.S. $	Can. $	U.K. £	Aust. $
BP-3a	1940/2	Dark maroon	450.00	575.00	250.00	600.00
BP-3a		Lilac	85.00	120.00	50.00	125.00
BP-3b		Dark maroon	450.00	575.00	250.00	600.00
BP-3b		Lilac	75.00	100.00	50.00	110.00
BP-3c		Lilac	75.00	100.00	50.00	110.00
BP-4		Lilac	85.00	115.00	55.00	125.00
BP-6a		Lilac	40.00	60.00	25.00	75.00
BP-10b		Lilac	36.00	65.00	18.00	70.00

Second version: Pipe in

MR. BENJAMIN BUNNY AND PETER RABBIT™

Modeller: Alan Maslankowski
Height: 4", 10.1 cm
Colour: Benjamin Bunny: lilac jacket, yellow waistcoat
Peter Rabbit: blue jacket
Issued: 1975 - 1995

Back Stamp	Beswick Number	Doulton Number	Price			
			U.S. $	Can. $	U.K. £	Aust. $
BP-3b	2509	P2509	200.00	250.00	125.00	275.00
BP-3c			175.00	225.00	100.00	250.00
BP-6a			75.00	100.00	50.00	100.00

MR. DRAKE PUDDLE-DUCK™

Modeller: David Lyttleton
Height: 4", 10.1 cm
Colour: White duck, blue
waistcoat and trousers
Issued: 1979 - 2000

BEATRIX POTTER
"Mr. Drake-Duck"
© Frederick Warne & Co. 1979
Licensed by Copyrights
BESWICK ENGLAND

Back Stamp	Beswick Number	Doulton Number	Price			
			U.S. $	Can. $	U.K. £	Aust. $
BP-3b	2628	P2628	75.00	90.00	40.00	95.00
BP-3c			90.00	115.00	50.00	120.00
BP-4			95.00	120.00	50.00	125.00
BP-6a			40.00	60.00	25.00	70.00
BP-10b			36.00	65.00	18.00	75.00

First version: Green toad

MR. JACKSON™

Modeller: Albert Hallam
Height: 2 ¾", 7.0 cm

FIRST VARIATION: GREEN TOAD

Colour: Green toad wearing mauve jacket
Issued: 1974 - c.1974

BEATRIX POTTER'S
"Mr Jackson"
F. Warne & Co. Ltd.
Copyright
BESWICK ENGLAND

Back Stamp	Beswick Number	Doulton Number	Price			
			U.S. $	Can. $	U.K. £	Aust. $
BP-3a	2453/1	P2453/1	550.00	750.00	325.00	700.00

Second version: Brown toad

SECOND VARIATION: BROWN TOAD

Colour: Brown toad wearing mauve jacket
Issued: 1975 - 1997

BEATRIX POTTER'S
"Mr Jackson"
F. Warne & Co. Ltd.
© Copyright 1974
BESWICK ENGLAND

Back Stamp	Beswick Number	Doulton Number	Price			
			U.S. $	Can. $	U.K. £	Aust. $
BP-3b	2453/2	P2453/2	75.00	100.00	55.00	115.00
BP-3c			95.00	125.00	65.00	135.00
BP-6a			60.00	75.00	35.00	75.00

MR. JEREMY FISHER™

Modeller: Arthur Gredington
Height: 3", 7.6 cm
Size: Small

FIRST VERSION: SMALL SIZE
FIRST VARIATION: SPOTTED LEGS

Colour: Lilac coat, green frog with small brown spots on head and legs
Issued: 1950 - c.1974

Back Stamp	Beswick Number	Doulton Number	Price			
			U.S. $	Can. $	U.K. £	Aust. $
BP-1	1157/1	P1157/1	400.00	525.00	250.00	550.00
BP-2			275.00	325.00	175.00	300.00
BP-3a			175.00	225.00	90.00	200.00
BP-3b			125.00	175.00	70.00	175.00

Small size, spotted legs

FIRST VERSION: SMALL SIZE
SECOND VARIATION: STRIPED LEGS

Colour: Lilac coat, green frog with large spots on head and stripes on legs
Issued: c.1950 to the present

Back Stamp	Beswick Number	Doulton Number	Price			
			U.S. $	Can. $	U.K. £	Aust. $
BP-1	1157/2	P1157/2	400.00	525.00	250.00	550.00
BP-3b			75.00	100.00	40.00	100.00
BP-3c			80.00	120.00	55.00	125.00
BP-6a			40.00	50.00	25.00	60.00
BP-10a			36.00	—	17.50	—

Note: BP-3c backstamp name exists with and without "Mr."

Small size, striped legs

SECOND VERSION: LARGE SIZE
FIRST VARIATION: LILAC BUTTONS

Modeller: Martyn Alcock
Height: 5", 12.7 cm
Size: Large
Colour: Lilac coat, green frog with stripes on legs
Issued: 1994 - 1997

Back Stamp	Beswick Number	Doulton Number	Price			
			U.S. $	Can. $	U.K. £	Aust. $
BP-6b	3372/1	P3372	65.00	95.00	30.00	100.00

SECOND VERSION: LARGE SIZE
SECOND VARIATION: GOLD BUTTONS

Colour: Green frog with stripes on legs, lilac coat with gold buttons
Issued: 1998 in a limited edition of 1,947
Series: Gold edition

Back Stamp	Beswick Number	Doulton Number	Price			
			U.S. $	Can. $	U.K. £	Aust. $
BP-9c	3372/2	PG3372	75.00	110.00	40.00	125.00

Note: Issued, numbered and sold as a pair with Tom Kitten, second version, second variation.

Large size, striped legs

MR. JEREMY FISHER DIGGING™

Modeller: Ted Chawner
Height: 3 ¾", 9.5 cm
Colour: Mauve coat, pink waistcoat, white cravat, green frog with brown highlights
Issued: 1988 - 1994

Back Stamp	Beswick Number	Doulton Number	Price U.S. $	Can. $	U.K. £	Aust. $
BP-4	3090	P3090	275.00	400.00	175.00	425.00
BP-6a			150.00	200.00	75.00	225.00

Note: Jeremy Fisher's skin may have dark or light spots.

MR. McGREGOR™

Modeller: Martyn Alcock
Height: 5 ¼", 13.5 cm
Colour: Brown hat and trousers, tan vest and pale blue shirt
Issued: 1995 to the present

Back Stamp	Beswick Number	Doulton Number	Price U.S. $	Can. $	U.K. £	Aust. $
BP-6a	3506/1	P3506/1	60.00	60.00	40.00	75.00
BP-10b			48.00	—	20.00	—

Note: A variety of this figure exists with the right arm at chest height.

MR. TOD™

Modeller: Ted Chawner
Height: 4 ¾", 12.1 cm
Colour: Green suit, red waistcoat, dark brown walking stick
Issued: 1988 - 1993

Back Stamp	Beswick Number	Doulton Number	Price U.S. $	Can. $	U.K. £	Aust. $
BP-4	3091/1	P3091/1	325.00	400.00	200.00	450.00
BP-6a			150.00	200.00	85.00	200.00

Note: Variations occur with the head facing right or left and the base in either green or brown.

MRS. FLOPSY BUNNY™

Modeller:	Arthur Gredington	
Height:	4", 10.1 cm	
Colour:	1. Dark blue dress, pink bag	
	2. Light blue dress, pink bag	
Issued:	1965 - 1998	

Back Stamp	Beswick Number	Colour Variation	U.S. $	Can. $	U.K. £	Aust. $
BP-2	1942	Dark blue	225.00	300.00	150.00	250.00
BP-3a		Dark blue	75.00	110.00	50.00	100.00
BP-3b		Dark blue	65.00	100.00	40.00	100.00
BP-3b		Light blue	65.00	100.00	40.00	100.00
BP-3c		Light blue	75.00	110.00	55.00	115.00
BP-4		Light blue	85.00	125.00	60.00	125.00
BP-6a		Light blue	55.00	75.00	35.00	75.00
BP-10b		Light blue	45.00	65.00	30.00	70.00

MRS. RABBIT™

Modeller:	Arthur Gredington
Height:	4 ¼", 10.8 cm
Size:	Small

FIRST VERSION: SMALL SIZE, UMBRELLA OUT

Colour:	1. Pink and yellow striped dress
	2. Lilac and pale green striped dress
Issued:	1951 - c.1974

Back Stamp	Beswick Number	Colour Variation	U.S. $	Can. $	U.K. £	Aust. $
BP-1	1200/1	Pink	550.00	725.00	325.00	750.00
BP-2		Pink	450.00	600.00	250.00	600.00
BP-2		Lilac	450.00	600.00	250.00	600.00
BP-3a		Lilac	325.00	425.00	150.00	425.00
BP-3b		Lilac	300.00	400.00	150.00	400.00

First version: Umbrella out

Note: The base of this figure is too small to carry the circular Beswick England backstamp. It is flattened and the copyright date is carried in script.

SECOND VERSION: SMALL SIZE UMBRELLA MOULDED TO DRESS

Colour:	Lilac and yellow striped dress, red collar and cap, light straw coloured basket
Issued:	c.1975 to the present

Back Stamp	Beswick Number	Doulton Number	U.S. $	Can. $	U.K. £	Aust. $
BP-3b	1200/2	P1200/2	75.00	100.00	50.00	100.00
BP-3c			80.00	110.00	60.00	115.00
BP-4			85.00	125.00	65.00	125.00
BP-6a			50.00	75.00	30.00	75.00
BP-10c			36.00	—	17.50	—

Second version: Umbrella moulded to dress

Brown umbrella point and handle

Gold umbrella point and handle

MRS. RABBIT™

Modeller:	Martyn Alcock
Height:	6 ¼", 15.9 cm
Size:	Large

THIRD VERSION: LARGE SIZE
FIRST VARIATION: BROWN UMBRELLA
POINT AND HANDLE

Colour:	White, pink, yellow and green
Issued:	1994 - 1997

ROYAL ALBERT ®
ENGLAND
Mrs Rabbit
Beatrix Potter
© F. WARNE & CO.1993
© 1993 ROYAL ALBERT LTD.

Back Stamp	Beswick Number	Doulton Number	Price			
			U.S. $	Can. $	U.K. £	Aust. $
BP-6b	3398/1	P3398	60.00	95.00	35.00	100.00

THIRD VERSION: LARGE SIZE
SECOND VARIATION: GOLD UMBRELLA
POINT AND HANDLE

Colour:	White, pink, yellow and green, gold umbrella point and handle
Issued:	1998 in a limited edition of 1,947
Series:	Gold edition

Back Stamp	Beswick Number	Doulton Number	Price			
			U.S. $	Can. $	U.K. £	Aust. $
BP-9c	3398/2	PG3398	60.00	95.00	40.00	100.00

Note: Issued, numbered and sold as a pair with Foxy Whiskered Gentleman, second version, second variation.

MRS. RABBIT AND BUNNIES™

Modeller:	David Lyttleton
Height:	3 ¾", 9.5 cm
Colour:	Blue dress with white apron, dark blue chair
Issued:	1976 - 1997

BEATRIX POTTER'S
Mrs. Rabbit and Bunnies
F. Warne & Co.Ltd.
© Copyright 1976
BESWICK ENGLAND

Back Stamp	Beswick Number	Doulton Number	Price			
			U.S. $	Can. $	U.K. £	Aust. $
BP-3b	2543	P2543	85.00	115.00	50.00	100.00
BP-3c			110.00	150.00	70.00	125.00
BP-4			110.00	150.00	70.00	125.00
BP-5			135.00	175.00	85.00	175.00
BP-6a			55.00	75.00	35.00	75.00

Potteries Antique Centre

Specialists in Collectable Ceramics

Our China Rooms house one of the largest collections of rare and discontinued ceramics in the country.

Amongst our vast stocks you will find all the famous names associated with the potteries.

Royal Doulton, Beswick, Wade, Wedgwood, Moorcroft. Crown Derby, Shelley, Carlton Ware, Minton, Clarice Cliff, Charlotte Rhead, Crown Devon, Coalport, Royal Winton, Paragon, Royal Worcester plus much more.

Visit Our Website: www.potteriesantiquecentre.com

Comprehensive Product List   Worldwide Mailorder Service
News and Future Events   Special Internet Deals

We also purchase complete collections or single items. Top prices paid instantly. Regular buying trips to USA & Canada.
bill@potteriesantiquecentre.com

OPEN SEVEN DAYS

Tell us your "Wants" if we don't have it, then we'll try and find it!

MRS. RABBIT AND PETER™

FIRST VERSION: SMALL SIZE

Modeller: Warren Platt
Height: 3 ½", 8.9 cm
Size: Small
Colour: Mrs. Rabbit: Pale blue dress, white apron
Peter: Pale blue coat, yellow buttons
Issued: 1997 to the present

Back Stamp	Beswick Number	Doulton Number	Price			
			U.S. $	Can. $	U.K. £	Aust. $
BP-6a	3646	P3646	65.00	90.00	35.00	90.00
BP-10b			72.00	—	29.00	—

SECOND VERSION: LARGE SIZE

Modeller: Amanda Hughes-Lubeck
Height: 5 ¼", 13.3 cm
Size: Large
Colour: Mrs. Rabbit: Pale blue dress; white apron
Peter: Pale blue coat with gold buttons
Issued: 1999 in a limited edition of 2,500

Back Stamp	Beswick Number	Doulton Number	Price			
			U.S. $	Can. $	U.K. £	Aust. $
BP-9c	3978	PG3978	—	—	80.00	—

First version: Small size

Second version: Large size, gold buttons

MRS. RABBIT COOKING™

Modeller: Martyn Alcock
Height: 4", 10.1 cm
Colour: Blue dress, white apron
Issued: 1992 - 1999

Back Stamp	Beswick Number	Doulton Number	Price			
			U.S. $	Can. $	U.K. £	Aust. $
BP-6a	3278	P3278	40.00	60.00	25.00	70.00
BP-10b			55.00	75.00	35.00	80.00

Small size, diagonal stripes

Small size, plaid

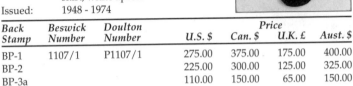

MRS. TIGGY-WINKLE™

Modeller: Arthur Gredington
Height: 3 ¼", 8.3 cm
Size: Small

FIRST VERSION: SMALL SIZE
FIRST VARIATION: DIAGONAL STRIPES

Colour: Diagonal striped red-brown and white dress, green and blue striped skirt, white apron
Issued: 1948 - 1974

Back Stamp	Beswick Number	Doulton Number	Price			
			U.S. $	Can. $	U.K. £	Aust. $
BP-1	1107/1	P1107/1	275.00	375.00	175.00	400.00
BP-2			225.00	300.00	125.00	325.00
BP-3a			110.00	150.00	65.00	150.00

Note: This figurine is also recognizable by the heavily patterned bustle.

FIRST VERSION: SMALL SIZE
SECOND VARIATION: PLAID

Colour: Red-brown and white plaid dress, green and blue striped skirt, white apron
Issued: 1972 - 2000

Back Stamp	Beswick Number	Doulton Number	Price			
			U.S. $	Can. $	U.K. £	Aust. $
BP-2	1107/2	P1107/2	225.00	300.00	150.00	275.00
BP-3a			100.00	150.00	65.00	115.00
BP-3b			65.00	95.00	40.00	85.00
BP-3c			100.00	150.00	65.00	115.00
BP-4			110.00	175.00	70.00	150.00
BP-6a			40.00	60.00	25.00	70.00
BP-10c			36.00	65.00	18.00	75.00

FIRST VERSION: SMALL SIZE
THIRD VARIATION: PLATINUM IRON

Colour: Red-brown and white dress, green and blue striped skirt, white apron, platinum iron
Issued: 1998 - 1998

Back Stamp	Beswick Number	Doulton Number	Price			
			U.S. $	Can. $	U.K. £	Aust. $
BP-9b	1107/3	PG1107	55.00	80.00	30.00	90.00

Small size, platinum iron

MRS. TIGGY-WINKLE™

Modeller: Amanda Hughes-Lubeck
Height: 4 ½", 11.9 cm
Size: Large

SECOND VERSION: LARGE SIZE
FIRST VARIATION: CREAMY-BROWN IRON

Colour: Brown and white striped dress, white apron, creamy-brown iron
Issued: 1996 - 1997

Back Stamp	Beswick Number	Doulton Number	Price			
			U.S. $	Can. $	U.K. £	Aust. $
BP-6b	3437/1	P3437	85.00	95.00	50.00	100.00

SECOND VERSION: LARGE SIZE
SECOND VARIATION: PLATINUM IRON

Colour: Brown and white striped dress, white apron, platinum iron
Issued: 1998 in a limited edition of 1,947
Series: Gold edition

Back Stamp	Beswick Number	Doulton Number	Price			
			U.S. $	Can. $	U.K. £	Aust. $
BP-9c	3437/2	PG3437	80.00	95.00	55.00	100.00

Note: Issued, numbered and sold as a pair with Jemima Puddle-Duck, second version, second variation.

Large size, creamy-brown iron

Large size, platinum iron

MRS. TIGGY WINKLE TAKES TEA™

Modeller: David Lyttleton
Height: 3 ¼", 8.3 cm
Colour: Pink and white dress, white and brown mob cap
Issued: 1985 to the present

Back Stamp	Beswick Number	Doulton Number	Price			
			U.S. $	Can. $	U.K. £	Aust. $
BP-3b	2877	P2877	100.00	125.00	65.00	115.00
BP-3c			100.00	125.00	65.00	115.00
BP-4			125.00	175.00	80.00	150.00
BP-6a			40.00	65.00	25.00	75.00
BP-10a			36.00	—	17.50	—

MRS. TIGGY-WINKLE WASHING™

Modeller:	David Lyttleton
Height:	2 ½", 6.4 cm
Colour:	Brown and white
Issued:	1998 - 2000

Back Stamp	Beswick Number	Doulton Number	Price U.S. $	Can. $	U.K. £	Aust. $
BP-8a	3789	P3789	200.00	300.00	100.00	300.00
BP-10a			36.00	60.00	17.00	75.00

Note: Approximately 1,800 pieces were issued with the BP-8a backstamp.

MRS. TITTLEMOUSE™
Style One

Modeller:	Arthur Gredington
Height:	3 ½", 8.9 cm
Colour:	White and red striped blouse, blue and white striped skirt
Issued:	1948 - 1993

Back Stamp	Beswick Number	Doulton Number	Price U.S. $	Can. $	U.K. £	Aust. $
BP-1	1103	P1103	300.00	425.00	175.00	450.00
BP-2			195.00	275.00	100.00	225.00
BP-3a			75.00	100.00	50.00	100.00
BP-3b			75.00	100.00	50.00	100.00
BP-3c			75.00	100.00	50.00	100.00
BP-6a			75.00	100.00	50.00	100.00

MRS. TITTLEMOUSE™
Style Two

Modeller:	Shane Ridge
Height:	3 ½", 8.9 cm
Colour:	White and red striped blouse, blue and white striped skirt, white apron
Issued:	2000 to the present

Back Stamp	Beswick Number	Doulton Number	Price U.S. $	Can. $	U.K. £	Aust. $
BP-10a	4015	P4015	48.00	—	30.00	—

NO MORE TWIST™

Modeller:	Martyn Alcock
Height:	3 ½", 9.2 cm
Colour:	Brown and white mouse
Issued:	1992 - 1997

Back Stamp	Beswick Number	Doulton Number	Price			
			U.S. $	Can. $	U.K. £	Aust. $
BP-6a	3325	P3325	65.00	95.00	30.00	100.00

OLD MR. BOUNCER™

Modeller:	David Lyttleton
Height:	3", 7.6 cm
Colour:	Brown jacket and trousers, blue scarf
Issued:	1986 - 1995

Back Stamp	Beswick Number	Doulton Number	Price			
			U.S. $	Can. $	U.K. £	Aust. $
BP-3c	2956	P2956	85.00	125.00	60.00	150.00
BP-6a			55.00	85.00	30.00	90.00

OLD MR. BROWN™

Modeller:	Albert Hallam
Height:	3 ¼", 8.3 cm
Colour:	1. Brown owl, red squirrel
	2. Orange owl, red squirrel
Issued:	1963 - 1999

Back Stamp	Beswick Number	Colour Variation	Price			
			U.S. $	Can. $	U.K. £	Aust. $
BP-2	1796	Brown	175.00	250.00	100.00	275.00
BP-3a		Brown	85.00	125.00	55.00	125.00
BP-3b		Brown	80.00	110.00	55.00	110.00
BP-3b		Orange	85.00	115.00	60.00	120.00
BP-3c		Orange	85.00	115.00	60.00	120.00
BP-6a		Orange	40.00	55.00	25.00	70.00
BP-10a		Orange	40.00	60.00	20.00	75.00

OLD MR. PRICKLEPIN™

Modeller:	David Lyttleton
Height:	2 ½", 6.4 cm
Colour:	Brown
Issued:	1983 - 1989

BEATRIX POTTER'S
"Old Mr Pricklepin"
© Frederick Warne P.L.C. 1983
BESWICK ENGLAND

Back Stamp	Beswick Number	Doulton Number	Price			
			U.S. $	Can. $	U.K. £	Aust. $
BP-3b	2767	P2767	100.00	125.00	60.00	110.00
BP-3c			125.00	150.00	70.00	125.00
BP-6a			135.00	175.00	85.00	175.00

First version: Small size

PETER AND THE RED POCKET HANDKERCHIEF™

Modeller:	Martyn Alcock
Height:	4 ¾", 12.3 cm
Size:	Small

FIRST VERSION: SMALL SIZE
FIRST VARIATION: YELLOW BUTTONS

Colour:	Light blue jacket with yellow buttons, red handkerchief
Issued:	1991 - 1999

ROYAL ALBERT ®
ENGLAND
Peter and the
Red Pocket Handkerchief
Beatrix Potter
© F. WARNE & CO. 1990
© 1990 ROYAL ALBERT LTD

Back Stamp	Beswick Number	Doulton Number	Price			
			U.S. $	Can. $	U.K. £	Aust. $
BP-6a	3242	P3242	50.00	75.00	25.00	80.00
BP-10a			50.00	75.00	20.00	80.00

FIRST VERSION: SMALL SIZE
SECOND VARIATION: GOLD BUTTONS

Colour:	Dark blue jacket with gold buttons, red handkerchief
Issued:	1997 - 1997

Back Stamp	Beswick Number	Doulton Number	Price			
			U.S. $	Can. $	U.K. £	Aust. $
BP-9d	5190	PG5190	75.00	125.00	50.00	135.00

Note: Peter Rabbit, first version, second variation was commissioned by Petter Rabbit and Friends.

Second version: Small size, gold buttons

PETER AND THE RED POCKET HANDKERCHIEF™

Modeller:	Amanda Hughes-Lubeck
Height:	7 ¼", 18.4 cm
Size:	Large

SECOND VERSION: LARGE SIZE
FIRST VARIATION: YELLOW BUTTONS

Colour:	Light blue coat with yellow buttons, red handkerchief
Issued:	1996 - 1997

Back Stamp	Beswick Number	Doulton Number	Price			
			U.S. $	Can. $	U.K. £	Aust. $
BP-6b	3592/1	P3592	85.00	110.00	40.00	110.00

Note: The backstamp on this version reads Peter "with" the Red Pocket Handkerchief.

Second version: Large size

SECOND VERSION: LARGE SIZE
SECOND VARIATION: GOLD BUTTONS

Colour:	Light blue coat with gold buttons, red handkerchief
Issued:	1998 in a limited edition of 1,947
Series:	Gold edition

Back Stamp	Beswick Number	Doulton Number	Price			
			U.S. $	Can. $	U.K. £	Aust. $
BP-9c	3592/2	PG3592	85.00	110.00	40.00	110.00

Note: Issued, numbered and sold as a pair with The Tailor of Gloucester, second version, second variation.

Second version: Large size, gold buttons

PETER ATE A RADISH™

Modeller:	Warren Platt
Height:	4", 10.1 cm
Colour:	Blue jacket, brown and white rabbit, red radishes
Issued:	1995 - 1998

Back Stamp	Beswick Number	Doulton Number	Price			
			U.S. $	Can. $	U.K. £	Aust. $
BP-6a	3533	P3533	40.00	65.00	25.00	75.00
BP-10b			40.00	65.00	25.00	75.00

Note: BP-10b was reported by Royal Doulton in the backstamp changeover in 1998. We need confirmation that this backstamp was used on an actual issued figure.

PETER IN BED™

Modeller:	Martyn Alcock
Height:	2 ¾", 7.0 cm
Colour:	Blue, white, pink and green
Issued:	1995 to the present

ROYAL ALBERT ®
ENGLAND
Peter in Bed
Beatrix Potter
© F. WARNE & CO. 1994
© 1994 ROYAL ALBERT LTD

Back Stamp	Beswick Number	Doulton Number	Price			
			U.S. $	Can. $	U.K. £	Aust. $
BP-6a	3473	P3473	45.00	65.00	25.00	75.00
BP-10a			48.00	—	21.50	—

PETER IN THE GOOSEBERRY NET™

Modeller:	David Lyttleton
Height:	2", 4.6 cm
Colour:	Brown and white rabbit wearing blue jacket, green netting
Issued:	1989 - 1995

ROYAL ALBERT ®
ENGLAND
Peter in the Gooseberry Net
Beatrix Potter
© F. WARNE & CO. 1989
© 1989 ROYAL ALBERT LTD

Back Stamp	Beswick Number	Doulton Number	Price			
			U.S. $	Can. $	U.K. £	Aust. $
BP-6a	3157	P3157	80.00	115.00	55.00	115.00

PETER IN THE WATERING CAN™

Modeller:	Warren Platt
Height:	5", 12.7 cm
Colour:	Brown rabbit in a green watering can
Issued:	1999 to the present

BESWICK
B
MADE IN ENGLAND
Peter in the Watering Can
Beatrix Potter
© F. WARNE & CO. 1999
© 1999 ROYAL DOULTON

Back Stamp	Beswick Number	Doulton Number	Price			
			U.S. $	Can. $	U.K. £	Aust. $
BP-10a	3940	P3940	48.00	95.00	25.00	—

PETER RABBIT™

Modeller: Arthur Gredington
Height: 4 ½", 11.4 cm
Size: Small

FIRST VERSION: SMALL SIZE
FIRST VARIATION: DEEP BLUE JACKET
Colour: Dark blue jacket with yellow
              buttons
Issued: 1948 - c.1980

Back Stamp	Beswick Number	Doulton Number	Price			
			U.S. $	Can. $	U.K. £	Aust. $
BP-1	1098/1	P1098/1	300.00	400.00	175.00	350.00
BP-2			275.00	350.00	150.00	300.00
BP-3a			125.00	175.00	85.00	135.00
BP-3b			100.00	150.00	65.00	125.00

Small size, deep blue jacket

FIRST VERSION: SMALL SIZE
SECOND VARIATION: LIGHT BLUE JACKET
Colour: Light blue jacket with yellow
              buttons
Issued: c.1980 to the present

Back Stamp	Beswick Number	Base Variation	Price			
			U.S. $	Can. $	U.K. £	Aust. $
BP-3b	1098/2	Short base	65.00	90.00	40.00	100.00
BP-3b		Long base	65.00	90.00	40.00	100.00
BP-3c		Long base	75.00	100.00	45.00	110.00
BP-4		Long base	85.00	125.00	50.00	135.00
BP-5		Long base	125.00	175.00	75.00	175.00
BP-6a		Long base	40.00	60.00	25.00	70.00
BP-10b		Long base	36.00	63.00	17.00	75.00

Small size, light blue jacket

FIRST VERSION: SMALL SIZE
THIRD VARIATION: LIGHT BLUE JACKET,
GOLD BUTTONS
Colour: Light blue jacket with gold buttons
Issued: 1997 - 1997

Back Stamp	Beswick Number	Doulton Number	Price			
			U.S. $	Can. $	U.K. £	Aust. $
BP-9b	1098/3	PG1098	55.00	80.00	30.00	85.00

Small size, gold buttons

Large size, yellow buttons

Large size, gold buttons

PETER RABBIT™

Modeller: Martyn Alcock
Height: 6 ¾", 17.1 cm
Size: Large

SECOND VERSION: LARGE SIZE
FIRST VARIATION: YELLOW BUTTONS

Colour: Light blue jacket, yellow buttons
Issued: 1993 - 1997

Back Stamp	Beswick Number	Doulton Number	U.S. $	Can. $	U.K. £	Aust. $
BP-6b	3356/1	P3356	65.00	90.00	45.00	100.00
BP-7	100th Anniversary		90.00	125.00	55.00	135.00

SECOND VERSION: LARGE SIZE
SECOND VARIATION: GOLD BUTTONS

Colour: Blue jacket with gold buttons
Issued: 1997 in a limited edtion of 1,947
Series: Gold edition

Back Stamp	Beswick Number	Doulton Number	U.S. $	Can. $	U.K. £	Aust. $
BP-9c	3356/2	PG3356	75.00	100.00	40.00	100.00

Note: The second variation of this model was issued, numbered and sold as a pair with Benjamin Bunny, fourth version, fourth variation.

PETER RABBIT GARDENING™

Modeller: Warren Platt
Height: 5", 12.7 cm
Colour: Blue jacket, brown shovel, basket of carrots
Issued: 1998 - 1999

Back Stamp	Beswick Number	Doulton Number	U.S. $	Can. $	U.K. £	Aust. $
BP-10b	3739	P3739	60.00	90.00	30.00	100.00

PETER WITH DAFFODILS™

Modeller:	Warren Platt	
Height:	4 ¾", 12.1 cm	
Colour:	Light blue coat, yellow daffodils	
Issued:	1996 - 1999	

Back Stamp	Beswick Number	Doulton Number	Price			
			U.S. $	Can. $	U.K. £	Aust. $
BP-6a	3597	P3597	45.00	75.00	25.00	85.00
BP-10b			50.00	90.00	25.00	100.00

PETER WITH POSTBAG™

Modeller:	Amanda Hughes-Lubeck	
Height:	4 ¾", 12.1 cm	
Colour:	Light brown rabbit and postbag, lilac jacket trimmed in red	
Issued:	1996 to the present	

Back Stamp	Beswick Number	Doulton Number	Price			
			U.S. $	Can. $	U.K. £	Aust. $
BP-6a	3591	P3591	45.00	75.00	25.00	85.00
BP-10b			48.00	—	21.00	—

PICKLES™

Modeller:	Albert Hallam	
Height:	4 ½", 11.4 cm	
Colour:	Black face dog with brown jacket and white apron, pink book	
Issued:	1971 - 1982	

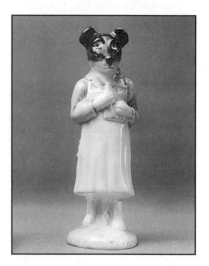

Back Stamp	Beswick Number	Doulton Number	Price			
			U.S. $	Can. $	U.K. £	Aust. $
BP-2	2334	P2334	700.00	1,000.00	450.00	1,000.00
BP-3a			475.00	700.00	300.00	700.00
BP-3b			425.00	600.00	275.00	600.00

First variation: Purple jacket

Second variation: Lilac jacket

PIGLING BLAND™

Modeller:	Graham Orwell
Height:	4 ¼", 10.8 cm

FIRST VARIATION: DEEP MAROON JACKET

Colour:	Purple jacket, blue waistcoat, yellow trousers
Issued:	1955 - 1974

Back Stamp	Beswick Number	Doulton Number	Price			
			U.S. $	Can. $	U.K. £	Aust. $
BP-2	1365/1	P1365/1	500.00	675.00	250.00	750.00
BP-3a			275.00	375.00	175.00	400.00
BP-3b			250.00	350.00	150.00	375.00

SECOND VARIATION: LILAC JACKET

Colour:	Lilac jacket, blue waistcoat, yellow trousers
Issued:	c.1975 - 1998

Back Stamp	Beswick Number	Doulton Number	Price			
			U.S. $	Can. $	U.K. £	Aust. $
BP-3b	1365/2	P1365/2	65.00	95.00	40.00	100.00
BP-3c			95.00	125.00	60.00	125.00
BP-6a			55.00	75.00	30.00	75.00
BP-10c			60.00	80.00	35.00	80.00

PIGLING EATS HIS PORRIDGE™

Modeller:	Martyn Alcock
Height:	4", 10.1 cm
Colour:	Brown coat, blue waistcoat and yellow trousers
Issued:	1991 - 1994

Back Stamp	Beswick Number	Doulton Number	Price			
			U.S. $	Can. $	U.K. £	Aust. $
BP-6a	3252	P3252	175.00	225.00	125.00	250.00

PIG-WIG™

Modeller:	Albert Hallam
Height:	4", 10.1 cm
Colour:	1. Grey pig, pale blue dress
	2. Black pig, deep blue dress
Issued:	1972 - 1982

Back Stamp	Beswick Number	Colour Variation	Price			
			U.S. $	Can. $	U.K. £	Aust. $
BP-2	2381	Grey pig	Extremely Rare			
BP-3a		Black pig	600.00	850.00	375.00	875.00
BP-3b		Black pig	575.00	800.00	350.00	825.00

POORLY PETER RABBIT™

Modeller:	David Lyttleton
Height:	3 ¾", 9.5 cm
Colour:	Brown-red and white blanket
Issued:	1976 - 1997

Back Stamp	Beswick Number	Doulton Number	Price			
			U.S. $	Can. $	U.K. £	Aust. $
BP-3b	2560	P2560	100.00	125.00	65.00	125.00
BP-3c			100.00	125.00	65.00	125.00
BP-4			115.00	150.00	75.00	150.00
BP-6a			60.00	85.00	35.00	85.00

Note: Later models have a lighter brown blanket.

REBECCAH PUDDLE-DUCK™

Modeller:	David Lyttleton
Height:	3 ¼", 8.3 cm
Colour:	White goose, pale blue coat and hat
Issued:	1981 - 2000

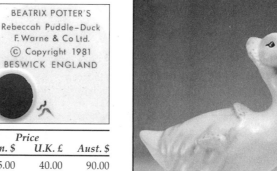

Back Stamp	Beswick Number	Doulton Number	Price			
			U.S. $	Can. $	U.K. £	Aust. $
BP-3b	2647	P2647	65.00	85.00	40.00	90.00
BP-3c			90.00	125.00	55.00	125.00
BP-4			95.00	140.00	55.00	140.00
BP-6a			35.00	50.00	20.00	65.00
BP-10b			36.00	65.00	18.00	75.00

RIBBY™

Modeller:	Arthur Gredington
Height:	3 ¼", 8.3 cm
Colour:	White dress with blue rings, white apron, pink and white striped shawl
Issued:	1951 - 2000

Back Stamp	Beswick Number	Doulton Number	Price			
			U.S. $	Can. $	U.K. £	Aust. $
BP-1	1199	P1199	325.00	450.00	200.00	425.00
BP-2			200.00	275.00	125.00	275.00
BP-3a			90.00	125.00	55.00	125.00
BP-3b			90.00	125.00	55.00	125.00
BP-3c			90.00	125.00	50.00	125.00
BP-6a			40.00	55.00	25.00	65.00
BP-10c			36.00	65.00	18.00	75.00

Note: The name shown on BP-6a and BP-10c is Mrs Ribby.

RIBBY AND THE PATTY PAN™

Modeller:	Martyn Alcock
Height:	3 ½", 8.9 cm
Colour:	Blue dress, white apron
Issued:	1992 - 1998

Back Stamp	Beswick Number	Doulton Number	Price			
			U.S. $	Can. $	U.K. £	Aust. $
BP-6a	3280	P3280	55.00	75.00	25.00	75.00

SALLY HENNY PENNY™

Modeller:	Albert Hallam
Height:	4", 10.1 cm
Colour:	Brown and gold chicken, black hat and cloak, two yellow chicks
Issued:	1974 - 1993

Back Stamp	Beswick Number	Doulton Number	Price			
			U.S. $	Can. $	U.K. £	Aust. $
BP-3a	2452	P2452	75.00	100.00	50.00	100.00
BP-3b			75.00	100.00	50.00	100.00
BP-3c			75.00	100.00	50.00	100.00
BP-6a			55.00	80.00	35.00	90.00

SAMUEL WHISKERS™

Modeller:	Arthur Gredington
Height:	3 ¼", 8.3 cm
Colour:	Light green coat, yellow waistcoat and trousers
Issued:	1948 - 1995

Back Stamp	Beswick Number	Doulton Number	Price			
			U.S. $	Can. $	U.K. £	Aust. $
BP-1	1106	P1106	275.00	400.00	175.00	425.00
BP-2			225.00	300.00	150.00	325.00
BP-3a			95.00	125.00	50.00	135.00
BP-3b			60.00	85.00	35.00	100.00
BP-3c			95.00	125.00	50.00	135.00
BP-4			95.00	125.00	50.00	135.00
BP-6a			95.00	125.00	50.00	135.00

SIMPKIN™

Modeller:	Alan Maslankowski
Height:	4", 10.1 cm
Colour:	Green coat
Issued:	1975 - 1983

Back Stamp	Beswick Number	Doulton Number	Price			
			U.S. $	Can. $	U.K. £	Aust. $
BP-3b	2508	P2508	750.00	1,000.00	450.00	1,000.00

SIR ISAAC NEWTON™

Modeller:	Graham Tongue
Height:	3 ¾", 9.5 cm
Colour:	Pale green jacket, yellow waistcoat with tan markings
Issued:	1973 - 1984

Back Stamp	Beswick Number	Doulton Number	Price			
			U.S. $	Can. $	U.K. £	Aust. $
BP-3a	2425	P2425	525.00	700.00	300.00	725.00
BP-3b			450.00	650.00	250.00	675.00

Note: The colour and size of Sir Isaac Newton may vary.

Small size, red-brown squirrel

Small size, golden brown squirrel

Large size, gold core

SQUIRREL NUTKIN™

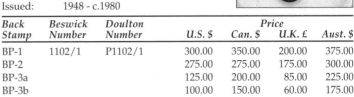

Modeller:	Arthur Gredington
Height:	3 ¾", 9.5 cm
Size:	Small

FIRST VERSION: SMALL SIZE
FIRST VARIATION: RED-BROWN SQUIRREL

Colour:	Red-brown squirrel, green-brown apple
Issued:	1948 - c.1980

Back Stamp	Beswick Number	Doulton Number	Price U.S. $	Can. $	U.K. £	Aust. $
BP-1	1102/1	P1102/1	300.00	350.00	200.00	375.00
BP-2			275.00	275.00	175.00	300.00
BP-3a			125.00	200.00	85.00	225.00
BP-3b			100.00	150.00	60.00	175.00

FIRST VERSION: SMALL SIZE
SECOND VARIATION: GOLDEN BROWN SQUIRREL

Colour:	Golden brown squirrel, green apple
Issued:	c.1980 - 2000

Back Stamp	Beswick Number	Doulton Number	Price U.S. $	Can. $	U.K. £	Aust. $
BP-3b	1102/2	P1102/2	65.00	90.00	40.00	95.00
BP-3c			95.00	135.00	60.00	150.00
BP-6a			40.00	50.00	25.00	65.00
BP-10a			36.00	63.00	17.50	70.00

SECOND VERSION: LARGE SIZE
RED CRAB APPLE, GOLD CORE

Modeller:	Amanda Hughes-Lubeck
Height:	5 ¼", 13.3 cm
Size:	Large
Colour:	Golden brown squirrel, red crab-apple, gold core
Issued:	1999 in a limited edition of 1,947
Series:	Gold edition

Back Stamp	Beswick Number	Doulton Number	Price U.S. $	Can. $	U.K. £	Aust. $
BP-9c	3893	PG3893	65.00	95.00	40.00	100.00

Note: The second version of Squirrel Nutkin was issued, numbered and sold as a pair with Hunca Munca Sweeping, second version.

SUSAN™

Modeller:	David Lyttleton
Height:	4", 10.1 cm
Colour:	Blue dress, green, pink and black shawl and hat
Issued:	1983 - 1989

BEATRIX POTTER
"Susan"
© F. Warne & Co. 1983
Licensed by Copyrights
BeS WICK ENGLAND

Back Stamp	Beswick Number	Doulton Number	Price			
			U.S. $	*Can. $*	*U.K. £*	*Aust. $*
BP-3b	2716	P2716	275.00	400.00	175.00	375.00
BP-3c			300.00	425.00	200.00	400.00
BP-6a			275.00	400.00	175.00	375.00

Note: The colour and size of Susan may vary.

SWEET PETER RABBIT™

Modeller:	Shane Ridge
Height:	4 ¾", 12.1 cm
Colour:	Beige and cream rabbit, blue jacket, green and beige base
Issued:	1999 in a special edition of 2,950

BESWICK
B
MADE IN ENGLAND ™
Sweet Peter Rabbit
Beatrix Potter
© F. WARNE & CO. 1999
© 1999 ROYAL DOULTON
SPECIAL GOLD EDITION OF 2,950
FOR
PETER RABBIT AND FRIENDS
© F.W. and Co. 1999

Back Stamp	Beswick Number	Doulton Number	Price			
			U.S. $	*Can. $*	*U.K. £*	*Aust. $*
BP-11	3888	P3888	90.00	140.00	50.00	150.00

Note: This figure was commissioned by Peter Rabbit and Friends to commemorate the Year of the Rabbit, 1999.

First variation: Blue striped top

Second variation: White top

TABITHA TWITCHIT™

Modeller: Arthur Gredington
Height: 3 ½", 8.9 cm

FIRST VARIATION: BLUE STRIPED TOP

Colour: Blue and white striped dress, white apron
Issued: 1961 - 1974

Back Stamp	Beswick Number	Doulton Number	Price			
			U.S. $	Can. $	U.K. £	Aust. $
BP-2	1676/1	P1676/1	325.00	450.00	175.00	425.00
BP-3a			250.00	300.00	150.00	325.00
BP-3b			200.00	250.00	125.00	250.00

SECOND VARIATION: WHITE TOP

Colour: Blue and white striped dress, white apron
Issued: c.1975 - 1995

Back Stamp	Beswick Number	Doulton Number	Price			
			U.S. $	Can. $	U.K. £	Aust. $
BP-3b	1676/2	P1676/2	75.00	100.00	50.00	100.00
BP-3c			75.00	100.00	50.00	100.00
BP-6a			75.00	100.00	50.00	100.00

Note: BP-3b and forward has Twitchit spelled "Twitchett."

TABITHA TWITCHIT AND MISS MOPPET™

FIRST VERSION: SMALL SIZE

Modeller:	David Lyttleton
Height:	3 ½", 8.9 cm
Size:	Small
Colour:	Lilac dress, white apron, yellow sponge and hassock
Issued:	1976 - 1993

BEATRIX POTTER'S
Tabitha Twitchit and Miss Moppet
F. Warne & Co.Ltd.
© Copyright 1976
BESWICK ENGLAND

Back Stamp	Beswick Number	Doulton Number	Price			
			U.S. $	Can. $	U.K. £	Aust. $
BP-3b	2544	P2544	225.00	275.00	150.00	275.00
BP-3c			225.00	275.00	150.00	275.00
BP-4			275.00	325.00	175.00	325.00
BP-6a			150.00	200.00	90.00	200.00

First version: Small size

TABITHA TWITCHIT AND MOPPET™

SECOND VERSION: LARGE SIZE

Modeller:	Martyn Alcock
Height:	5 ½" 14.0 cm
Size:	Large
Colour:	Tabitha Twitchit: Lilac dress and white apron
	Moppet: Grey striped kitten
	Stool: Yellow with gold legs
Issued:	2000 in a limited edition of 2,000
Series:	Gold edition

Back Stamp	Beswick Number	Doulton Number	Price			
			U.S. $	Can. $	U.K. £	Aust. $
BP-9c	4020	PG4020	—	—	80.00	—

Second version: Large size

First version, Small size

Second version: Large size

Second version: Large size, gold accents

TAILOR OF GLOUCESTER™
FIRST VERSION: SMALL SIZE

Modeller:	Arthur Gredington
Height:	3 ½", 8.9 cm
Size:	Small
Colour:	Brown mouse, yellow bobbin of red thread
Issued:	1949 to the present

Back Stamp	Beswick Number	Doulton Number	Price			
			U.S. $	Can. $	U.K. £	Aust. $
BP-1	1108	P1108	300.00	425.00	175.00	425.00
BP-2			200.00	300.00	125.00	300.00
BP-3a			65.00	90.00	40.00	95.00
BP-3b			65.00	90.00	40.00	95.00
BP-3c			65.00	90.00	40.00	95.00
BP-4			75.00	100.00	50.00	110.00
BP-6a			40.00	55.00	25.00	65.00
BP-10c			36.00	—	17.50	—

SECOND VERSION: LARGE SIZE
FIRST VARIATION: STANDARD COLOURS

Modeller:	Arthur Gredington
Height:	6", 15.0 cm
Size:	Large
Colour:	Brown mouse, yellow bobbin of red thread
Issued:	1995 - 1997

Back Stamp	Beswick Number	Doulton Number	Price			
			U.S. $	Can. $	U.K. £	Aust. $
BP-6b	3449/1	P3449	70.00	95.00	40.00	100.00

SECOND VERSION: LARGE SIZE
SECOND VARIATION: GOLD ACCENTS

Colour:	Brown mouse, yellow bobbin of red thread, gold accents
Issued:	1998 in a limited edition of 1,947
Series:	Gold edition

Back Stamp	Beswick Number	Doulton Number	Price			
			U.S. $	Can. $	U.K. £	Aust. $
BP-9c	3449/2	PG3449	70.00	95.00	40.00	100.00

Note: The second version, second variation of this model was issued, numbered and sold as a pair with Peter Rabbit and the Red Pocket Handkerchief, second version, second variation.

THE OLD WOMAN WHO LIVED IN A SHOE™

Modeller: Colin Melbourne
Size: 2 ¾" x 3 ¾", 7.0 cm x 9.5 cm
Colour: Blue shoe
Issued: 1959 - 1998

Back Stamp	Beswick Number	Doulton Number	Price			
			U.S. $	Can. $	U.K. £	Aust. $
BP-2	1545	P1545	225.00	325.00	135.00	325.00
BP-3a			85.00	125.00	60.00	125.00
BP-3b			60.00	85.00	40.00	90.00
BP-3c			85.00	125.00	60.00	125.00
BP-6a			60.00	80.00	30.00	70.00

THE OLD WOMAN WHO LIVED IN A SHOE KNITTING™

Modeller: David Lyttleton
Height: 3", 7.5 cm
Colour: Purple dress, white apron,
           pale blue shawl and mob cap,
           yellow chair
Issued: 1983 to the present

Back Stamp	Beswick Number	Doulton Number	Price			
			U.S. $	Can. $	U.K. £	Aust. $
BP-3b	2804	P2804	225.00	325.00	150.00	325.00
BP-3c			225.00	325.00	150.00	325.00
BP-6a			45.00	60.00	25.00	65.00
BP-10a			36.00	—	17.50	—

THIS PIG HAD A BIT OF MEAT™

Modeller: Martyn Alcock
Height: 4", 10.1 cm
Colour: Lilac dress, grey shawl,
           white apron and cap,
           gold-framed spectacles
Issued: 2000 in a special edition of 1,500

Back Stamp	Beswick Number	Doulton Number	Price			
			U.S. $	Can. $	U.K. £	Aust. $
BP-9d	4030	P4030	—	—	80.00	—

Note: Commissioned by Peter Rabbit and Friends.

THOMASINA TITTLEMOUSE™

Modeller:	David Lyttleton
Height:	3 ¼", 8.3 cm
Colour:	Brown and pink highlights
Issued:	1981 - 1989

Correct   Error

Backstamp Variations

Back Stamp	Beswick Number	Doulton Number	Price			
			U.S. $	Can. $	U.K. £	Aust. $
BP-3b	2668	P2668	125.00	175.00	85.00	200.00
BP-3c	Error		150.00	200.00	100.00	225.00
BP-6a			65.00	85.00	40.00	100.00

First variation: Red jacket

TIMMY TIPTOES™

Modeller:	Arthur Gredington
Height:	3 ¾", 9.5 cm

FIRST VARIATION: RED JACKET

Colour:	1. Brown-grey squirrel, red jacket
	2. Grey squirrel, red jacket
Issued:	1948 - c.1980

Back Stamp	Beswick Number	Colour Variation	Price			
			U.S. $	Can. $	U.K. £	Aust. $
BP-1	1101/1	Brown-grey	250.00	350.00	150.00	375.00
BP-1		Grey	250.00	350.00	150.00	375.00
BP-2		Brown-grey	200.00	300.00	120.00	325.00
BP-2		Grey	200.00	300.00	120.00	325.00
BP-3a		Brown-grey	150.00	200.00	85.00	225.00
BP-3a		Grey	150.00	200.00	85.00	225.00
BP-3b		Brown-grey	125.00	175.00	75.00	200.00
BP-3b		Grey	125.00	175.00	75.00	200.00

Second variation: Pink jacket

SECOND VARIATION: LIGHT PINK JACKET

Colour:	Grey squirrel, pink jacket
Issued:	c.1970 - 1997

Back Stamp	Beswick Number	Doulton Number	Price			
			U.S. $	Can. $	U.K. £	Aust. $
BP-2	1101/2	P1101/2	250.00	350.00	150.00	375.00
BP-3b			75.00	100.00	50.00	110.00
BP-3c			75.00	100.00	50.00	110.00
BP-6a			65.00	85.00	25.00	85.00

Note: Second variations will vary in colour in a similar manner as the first.

TIMMY WILLIE FETCHING MILK™

Modeller:	Warren Platt
Height:	3 ¼", 8.3 cm
Colour:	Brown and white mouse, blue milk jug
Issued:	2000 to the present

Back Stamp	Beswick Number	Doulton Number	Price			
			U.S. $	Can. $	U.K. £	Aust. $
BP-10a	3976	P3976	48.00	100.00	22.00	—

TIMMY WILLIE FROM JOHNNY TOWN-MOUSE™

Modeller:	Arthur Gredington
Height:	2 ½", 6.4 cm
Colour:	Brown and white mouse, green or multicoloured base
Issued:	1949 - 1993

Back Stamp	Beswick Number	Doulton Number	Price			
			U.S. $	Can. $	U.K. £	Aust. $
BP-1	1109	P1109	250.00	350.00	150.00	375.00
BP-2			175.00	275.00	125.00	300.00
BP-3a			75.00	100.00	45.00	105.00
BP-3b			55.00	80.00	35.00	85.00
BP-3c			65.00	90.00	40.00	95.00
BP-4			75.00	100.00	45.00	110.00
BP-6a			80.00	100.00	55.00	100.00

TIMMY WILLIE SLEEPING™

Modeller:	Graham Tongue
Size:	1 ¼" x 3 ¾", 3.2 cm x 9.5 cm
Colour:	Green, white and brown
Issued:	1986 - 1996

Back Stamp	Beswick Number	Doulton Number	Price			
			U.S. $	Can. $	U.K. £	Aust. $
BP-3c	2996	P2996	200.00	275.00	125.00	275.00
BP-6a			65.00	85.00	30.00	95.00

Small size, deep blue colourway

Small size, light blue colourway

Small size, gold buttons

TOM KITTEN™

Modeller:	Arthur Gredington
Height:	3 ½", 8.9 cm
Size:	Small

FIRST VERSION: SMALL SIZE
FIRST VARIATION: DEEP BLUE OUTFIT

Colour: Tabby kitten wearing deep blue jacket and trousers, dark green base
Issued: 1948 - c.1980

Back Stamp	Beswick Number	Doulton Number	U.S. $	Can. $	U.K. £	Aust. $
BP-1	1100/1	P1100/1	275.00	400.00	175.00	425.00
BP-2			225.00	300.00	125.00	300.00
BP-3a			90.00	125.00	60.00	125.00
BP-3b			90.00	125.00	50.00	125.00

FIRST VERSION: SMALL SIZE
SECOND VARIATION: LIGHT BLUE OUTFIT

Colour: Tabby kitten wearing light blue jacket and trousers, light green base
Issued: c.1980 - 1999

Back Stamp	Beswick Number	Doulton Number	U.S. $	Can. $	U.K. £	Aust. $
BP-3b	1100/2	P1100/2	90.00	115.00	50.00	115.00
BP-3c			80.00	100.00	45.00	100.00
BP-4			90.00	115.00	50.00	115.00
BP-6a			40.00	55.00	20.00	65.00
BP-10c			50.00	65.00	25.00	70.00

FIRST VERSION: SMALL SIZE
THIRD VARIATION: GOLD BUTTONS

Colour: Tabby kitten wearing light blue trousers and jacket with gold buttons
Issued: 1997 - 1997

Back Stamp	Beswick Number	Doulton Number	U.S. $	Can. $	U.K. £	Aust. $
BP-9b	1100/3	PG1100	75.00	95.00	30.00	100.00

Note: The small version of Tom Kitten was issued with two different style bases.

TOM KITTEN™

SECOND VERSION: LARGE SIZE
FIRST VARIATION: YELLOW BUTTONS

Modeller:	Martyn Alcock
Height:	5 ¼", 13.3 cm
Size:	Large
Colour:	Tabby kitten wearing light blue trousers and jacket, light green base
Issued:	1994 - 1997

Back Stamp	Beswick Number	Doulton Number	Price			
			U.S. $	Can. $	U.K. £	Aust. $
BP-7	3405/1	P3405	65.00	95.00	40.00	100.00

SECOND VERSION: LARGE SIZE
SECOND VARIATION: GOLD BUTTONS

Colour:	Light blue jacket and trousers, gold buttons
Issued:	1994 - 1997
Series:	Gold edition

Large size, yellow buttons

Back Stamp	Beswick Number	Doulton Number	Price			
			U.S. $	Can. $	U.K. £	Aust. $
BP-9c	3405/2	PG3405	75.00	100.00	55.00	110.00

Note: The second variation was issued, numbered and sold as a pair with Mr. Jeremy Fisher, second version, second variation.

TOM KITTEN AND BUTTERFLY™

Modeller:	Ted Chawner
Height:	3 ½", 8.9 cm
Colour:	Blue outfit, yellow hat
Issued:	1987 - 1994

Back Stamp	Beswick Number	Doulton Number	Price			
			U.S. $	Can. $	U.K. £	Aust. $
BP-3c	3030	P3030	350.00	475.00	200.00	475.00
BP-6a			200.00	275.00	150.00	275.00

TOM KITTEN IN THE ROCKERY™

Modeller:	Warren Platt
Height:	3 ½", 8.9 cm
Colour:	Pale blue jacket and trousers, yellow hat
Issued:	1998 to the present

Back Stamp	Beswick Number	Doulton Number	Price			
			U.S. $	Can. $	U.K. £	Aust. $
BP-10a	3719	P3719	36.00	60.00	18.00	65.00

TOM THUMB™

Modeller:	Warren Platt
Height:	3 ¼", 8.3 cm
Colour:	Rose-pink and yellow chimney
Issued:	1987 - 1997

BEATRIX POTTER
"Tom Thumb"
© F. Warne & Co. 1987
Licensed by Copyrights
BESWICK ENGLAND

Back Stamp	Beswick Number	Doulton Number	Price			
			U.S. $	Can. $	U.K. £	Aust. $
BP-3c	2989	P2989	165.00	225.00	115.00	225.00
BP-6a			55.00	75.00	35.00	75.00

TOMMY BROCK™

Modeller: Graham Orwell
Height: 3 ½", 8.9 cm

FIRST VERSION: SPADE HANDLE OUT
FIRST VARIATION: SMALL EYE PATCH

Colour: Blue jacket, pink waistcoat,
               yellow-green trousers
Issued: 1955 - 1974

Back Stamp	Beswick Number	Doulton Number	U.S. $	Can. $	U.K. £	Aust. $
BP-1a	1348/1	P1348/1		Extremely rare		
BP-2	1348/1	P1348/1	550.00	750.00	275.00	775.00
BP-3a			450.00	650.00	225.00	650.00

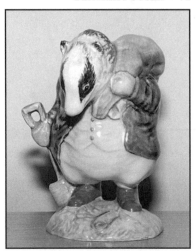

Handle out, small eye patch

FIRST VERSION: SPADE HANDLE OUT
SECOND VARIATION: LARGE EYE PATCH

Colour: Blue jacket, pink waistcoat,
               yellow trousers
Issued: c.1970 - c.1974

Back Stamp	Beswick Number	Doulton Number	U.S. $	Can. $	U.K. £	Aust. $
BP-2	1348/2	P1348/2	550.00	750.00	275.00	775.00
BP-3a			450.00	650.00	225.00	650.00

Handle out, large eye patch

Handle in, small eye patch

Handle in, large eye patch

TOMMY BROCK™

Modeller:	Graham Orwell
Height:	3 ½", 8.9 cm
Colour:	Blue-grey jacket, pink waistcoat, yellow trousers
Issued:	c.1974 - 1976

SECOND VERSION: HANDLE IN
FIRST VARIATION: SMALL EYE PATCH

Back Stamp	Beswick Number	Doulton Number	Price			
			U.S. $	Can. $	U.K. £	Aust. $
BP-3a	1348/3	P1348/3	150.00	225.00	85.00	250.00
BP-3b			125.00	200.00	75.00	225.00

SECOND VERSION: HANDLE IN
SECOND VARIATION: LARGE EYE PATCH

Colour:	Blue-grey jacket, red waistcoat, yellow trousers
Issued:	c.1975 to the present

Back Stamp	Beswick Number	Doulton Number	Price			
			U.S. $	Can. $	U.K. £	Aust. $
BP-3b	1348/4	P1348/4	65.00	95.00	40.00	100.00
BP-3c			80.00	115.00	50.00	120.00
BP-4			85.00	125.00	50.00	125.00
BP-6a			45.00	65.00	25.00	65.00
BP-10a			36.00	—	17.00	—

Note: The jacket colour varies from pale to dark blue in BP-3b.

YOCK-YOCK IN THE TUB™

Modeller:	Warren Platt
Height:	3", 7.6 cm
Colour:	Pink pig, brown tub
Issued:	2000 to the present

Back Stamp	Beswick Number	Doulton Number	Price			
			U.S. $	Can. $	U.K. £	Aust. $
BP-10a	3946	P3946	60.00	100.00	28.00	—

BEATRIX POTTER

TABLEAUX

TABLEAUX

DUCHESS AND RIBBY™

Modeller:	Martyn Alcock
Length:	7 ¾", 19.7 cm
Colour:	Black, lilac, grey and gold
Issued:	2000 in a limited edition of 1,500
Series:	Tableau

Back Stamp	Beswick Number	Doulton Number	U.S. $	Can. $	U.K. £	Aust. $
BP-9d	3983	P3983	—	—	195.00	—

Note: This figure was commissioned by Peter Rabbit and Friends.

GINGER AND PICKLES™

Modeller:	David Lyttleton
Height:	3 ¾", 9.5 cm
Colour:	Green, white and brown
Issued:	1998 in a limited edition of 2,750
Series:	Tableau

Back Stamp	Beswick Number	Doulton Number	U.S. $	Can. $	U.K. £	Aust. $
BP-9d	3790	P3790	350.00	525.00	175.00	550.00

Note: This figure was commissioned by Peter Rabbit and Friends.

HIDING FROM THE CAT™

Modeller:	Graham Tongue
Height:	5", 12.7 cm
Colour:	Brown, blue and grey
Issued:	1998 in a limited edition of 3,500
Series:	Tableau of the Year

Back Stamp	Beswick Number	Doulton Number	U.S. $	Can. $	U.K. £	Aust. $
BP-8c	3672	P3672	225.00	325.00	150.00	350.00

MITTENS, TOM KITTEN AND MOPPET™

Modeller:	Amanda Hughes-Lubeck
Length:	7", 17.8 cm
Colour:	Pale blue and beige
Issued:	1999 - 1999
Series:	Tableau of the Year

Back Stamp	Beswick Number	Doulton Number	Price			
			U.S. $	Can. $	U.K. £	Aust. $
BP-8c	3792	P3792	225.00	375.00	125.00	400.00

MRS. RABBIT AND THE FOUR BUNNIES™

Modeller:	Shane Ridge
Height:	4 ½", 11.9 cm
Colour:	Mrs Rabbit: Pale blue dress, white apron Bunnies: Rose cloaks Peter: Pale blue jacket
Issued:	1997 in a limited edition of 1,997
Series:	Tableau of the Year

Back Stamp	Beswick Number	Doulton Number	Price			
			U.S. $	Can. $	U.K. £	Aust. $
BP-8b	3672	P3672	550.00	750.00	350.00	800.00

MRS. TIGGY-WINKLE AND LUCIE™

Modeller:	Martyn Alcock
Height:	4", 10.1 cm
Colour:	Mrs. Tiggy-Winkle: Brown, pink and cream dress, yellow and blue striped skirt, white apron, red handkerchief, platinum iron and horseshoe, Lucie: Pink dress, white pinafore
Issued:	1999 in a limited edition of 2,950
Series:	Tableau

Back Stamp	Beswick Number	Doulton Number	Price			
			U.S. $	Can. $	U.K. £	Aust. $
BP-9d	3867	P3867	250.00	350.00	125.00	375.00

Note: Commissioned by Peter Rabbit and Friends.

PETER AND BENJAMIN PICKING ONIONS™

Modeller: Martyn Alcock
Height: 5", 12.7 cm
Colour: Peter: Pale blue jacket
             Benjamin: Brown jacket
Issued: 2000 in a limited edition of 3,000
Series: Tableau of the Year

Back Stamp	Beswick Number	Doulton Number	Price U.S. $	Can. $	U.K. £	Aust. $
BP-8c	3930	P3930	215.00	380.00	110.00	—

ALICE IN WONDERLAND™
BESWICK EARTHENWARE SERIES 1973-1983

Mad Hatter, Style One

Alice, Style One

White Rabbit, Style One

Dodo, Style One

Gryphon

Mock Turtle

Queen of Hearts, Style One

Fish Footman

King of Hearts

BEATRIX POTTER™

Ginger

Mr. Drake Puddle-Duck

Peter with Daffodils

Peter with Postbag

Foxy Whiskered Gentleman,
First Version

Peter and the Red Pocket Handkerchief,
Second Version, First Variation

BEATRIX POTTER™

Anna Maria

Goody Tiptoes

Little Pig Robinson Spying

Samuel Whiskers

Peter in Bed

Jemima Puddle-Duck, First Version,
Second Variation

Flopsy, Mopsy and Cottontail

The Old Woman Who Lived in a
Shoe Knitting

Gentleman Mouse Made a Bow

BEATRIX POTTER™

Tabitha Twitchit and Miss Moppet,
First Version

Hunca Munca

Goody and Timmy Tiptoes

Diggory Diggory Delvet

Timmy Willie from Johnny Town-Mouse

Old Mr. Pricklepin

Lady Mouse

Mrs. Rabbit and Bunnies

Mrs. Tittlemouse, Style One

BEATRIX POTTER™

Benjamin Bunny Sat on a Bank,
Second Version

Tom Kitten and Butterfly

Tailor of Gloucester, First Version

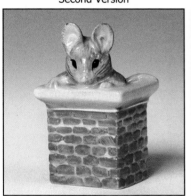

Tom Thumb

Poorly Peter Rabbit

Chippy Hackee

Cousin Ribby

Cottontail

Ribby

BEATRIX POTTER™

Lady Mouse made a Curtsy

Old Mr. Bouncer

And this Pig had None

Johnny Town-Mouse with Bag

Ribby and the Patty Pan

Simpkin

Pigling Eats His Porridge

Miss Dormouse

Foxy Reading Country News

BEATRIX POTTER™ TABLEAUX

Ginger and Pickles

Hiding from the Cat

Mrs. Rabbit and the Four Bunnies

Mrs. Tiggy-Winkle and Lucie

BEATRIX POTTER™ MISCELLANEOUS ITEMS
CHARACTER JUGS

Peter Rabbit

Tom Kitten

Jemima Puddle-Duck

STUDIO SCULPTURES

Mrs. Tiggy-Winkle

Peter Rabbit in the Watering Can

Flopsy Bunnies

WALL PLAQUES

Mrs. Tittlemouse

Peter Rabbit, Second Version

Jemima Puddle-Duck with Foxy
Whiskered Gentleman

BEATRIX POTTER MISCELLANEOUS

CHARACTER JUGS
PLAQUES
STANDS

CHARACTER JUGS

JEMIMA PUDDLE-DUCK CHARACTER JUG™

Modeller:	Ted Chawner
Height:	4", 10.1 cm
Colour:	Blue, pink and white
Issued:	1989 - 1992

BEATRIX POTTER
"Jemima Puddle-Duck"
© F. Warne & Co. 1988
Licensed by Copyrights
John Beswick
Studio of Royal Doulton
England

Back Stamp	Beswick Number	Doulton Number	Price			
			U.S. $	Can. $	U.K. £	Aust. $
BP-4	3088	P3088	225.00	275.00	125.00	250.00
BP-6a			200.00	250.00	100.00	225.00

MR. JEREMY FISHER CHARACTER JUG™

Modeller:	Graham Tongue
Height:	3", 7.6 cm
Colour:	Mauve
Issued:	1987 - 1992

John Beswick
ENGLAND
BEATRIX POTTER
"Jeremy Fisher"
© 1987 Frederick Warne & Co.
Licensed by Copyrights

Back Stamp	Beswick Number	Doulton Number	Price			
			U.S. $	Can. $	U.K. £	Aust. $
BP-4	2960	P2960	225.00	275.00	125.00	250.00
BP-6a			200.00	250.00	100.00	225.00

MRS. TIGGY-WINKLE CHARACTER JUG™

Modeller:	Ted Chawner
Height:	3", 7.6 cm
Colour:	White dress with brown stripes
Issued:	1988 - 1992

BEATRIX POTTER
"Mrs.Tiggy-Winkle"
© F. Warne & Co. 1988
Licensed by Copyrights
John Beswick
Studio of Royal Doulton
England

Back Stamp	Beswick Number	Doulton Number	Price			
			U.S. $	Can. $	U.K. £	Aust. $
BP-4	3102	P3102	225.00	275.00	125.00	250.00
BP-6a			200.00	250.00	100.00	225.00

OLD MR. BROWN
CHARACTER JUG™

Modeller: Graham Tongue
Height: 3", 7.6 cm
Colour: Brown and cream
Issued: 1987 - 1992

Back Stamp	Beswick Number	Doulton Number	Price			
			U.S. $	Can. $	U.K. £	Aust. $
BP-4	2959	P2959	250.00	275.00	125.00	250.00
BP-6a			200.00	250.00	100.00	225.00

PETER RABBIT
CHARACTER JUG™

Modeller: Graham Tongue
Height: 3", 7.6 cm
Colour: Brown, blue and white
Issued: 1987 - 1992

Back Stamp	Beswick Number	Doulton Number	Price			
			U.S. $	Can. $	U.K. £	Aust. $
BP-4	3006	P3006	200.00	275.00	100.00	250.00
BP-6a			250.00	325.00	150.00	300.00

TOM KITTEN
CHARACTER JUG™

Modeller: Ted Chawner
Height: 3", 7.6 cm
Colour: Brown, blue and white
Issued: 1989 - 1992

Back Stamp	Beswick Number	Doulton Number	Price			
			U.S. $	Can. $	U.K. £	Aust. $
BP-4	3103	P3103	225.00	300.00	125.00	275.00
BP-6a			275.00	375.00	175.00	350.00

PLAQUES

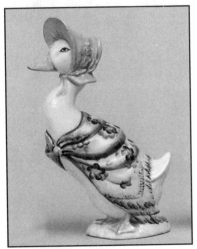

JEMIMA PUDDLE-DUCK PLAQUE™

Modeller:	Albert Hallam
Height:	6", 15.2 cm
Colour:	White duck, mauve shawl, pale blue bonnet
Issued:	1967 - 1969

Back Stamp	Beswick Number	Doulton Number	Price			
			U.S. $	Can. $	U.K. £	Aust. $
BP-2	2082	P2082	2,000.00	2,750.00	1,200.00	3,000.00

JEMIMA PUDDLE-DUCK WITH FOXY WHISKERED GENTLEMAN PLAQUE™

Modeller:	Harry Sales and David Lyttleton
Size:	7 ½" x 7 ½", 19.1 cm x 19.1 cm
Colour:	Brown, green, white and blue
Issued:	1977 - 1982

Back Stamp	Beswick Number	Doulton Number	Price			
			U.S. $	Can. $	U.K. £	Aust. $
BP-3	2594	P2594	175.00	225.00	100.00	250.00

MRS. TITTLEMOUSE PLAQUE™

Modeller:	Harry Sales
Height:	7 ½" x 7 ½", 19.1 cm x 19.1 cm
Colour:	Blue, pink and green
Issued:	1982 - 1984

Back Stamp	Beswick Number	Doulton Number	Price			
			U.S. $	Can. $	U.K. £	Aust. $
BP-3	2685	P2685	175.00	225.00	100.00	250.00

PETER RABBIT PLAQUE™
First Version

Modeller:	Graham Tongue
Height:	6", 15.2 cm
Colour:	Brown rabbit wearing a blue coat
Issued:	1967 - 1969

Back Stamp	Beswick Number	Doulton Number	Price			
			U.S. $	Can. $	U.K. £	Aust. $
BP-2	2083	P2083		Extremely rare		

PETER RABBIT PLAQUE™
Second Version

Modeller:	Harry Sales and David Lyttleton
Size:	7 ½" x 7 ½", 19.1 cm x 19.1 cm
Colour:	Blue, green, brown and orange
Issued:	1979 - 1983

Back Stamp	Beswick Number	Doulton Number	Price			
			U.S. $	Can. $	U.K. £	Aust. $
BP-3	2650	P2650	175.00	225.00	100.00	250.00

TOM KITTEN PLAQUE™

Modeller:	Graham Tongue
Height:	6", 15.2 cm
Colour:	Unknown
Issued:	1967 - 1969

Back Stamp	Beswick Number	Doulton Number	Price			
			U.S. $	Can. $	U.K. £	Aust. $
BP-2	2085	P2085	2,000.00	2,750.00	1,100.00	3,000.00

STANDS

DISPLAY STAND

Modeller:	Andrew Brindley
Size:	12 ½" x 12 ½", 31.7 cm x 31.7 cm
Colour:	Brown, light brown
Issued:	1970 - 1997

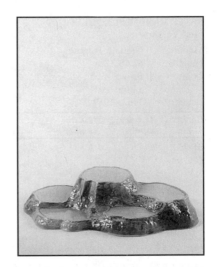

Back Stamp	Beswick Number	Doulton Number	Price			
			U.S. $	Can. $	U.K. £	Aust. $
Beswick	2295	P2295	75.00	100.00	50.00	100.00
Doulton			50.00	65.00	25.00	65.00

TREE LAMP BASE™

Modeller:	Albert Hallam and James Hayward
Height:	7", 17.8 cm
Colour:	Brown and green
Issued:	1958 - 1982

Back Stamp	Beswick Number	Doulton Number	Price			
			U.S. $	Can. $	U.K. £	Aust. $
BP-2	1531	P1531	400.00	475.00	200.00	450.00
BP-3			325.00	375.00	150.00	350.00

Note: The price of this lamp will vary in accordance with the figurine found attached to the base.

BEATRIX POTTER

RESIN STUDIO SCULPTURES

SS1
TIMMY WILLIE™

Designer: Harry Sales
Modeller: Graham Tongue
Height: 4 ¼", 10.8 cm
Colour: Green and brown
Issued: 1985 - 1985

Beswick Number	Price			
	U.S. $	Can. $	U.K. £	Aust. $
SS1	125.00	175.00	80.00	175.00

SS2
FLOPSY BUNNIES™

Designer: Harry Sales
Modeller: Graham Tongue
Height: 5", 12.7 cm
Colour: Browns and green
Issued: 1985 - 1985

Beswick Number	Price			
	U.S. $	Can. $	U.K. £	Aust. $
SS2	125.00	175.00	85.00	175.00

SS3
MR. JEREMY FISHER™

Designer: Harry Sales
Modeller: David Lyttleton
Height: 4", 10.1 cm
Colour: Beige, green and cream
Issued: 1985 - 1985

Beswick Number	Price			
	U.S. $	Can. $	U.K. £	Aust. $
SS3	125.00	175.00	80.00	200.00

SS4
PETER RABBIT™

Designer:	Harry Sales
Modeller:	Graham Tongue
Height:	7", 17.8 cm
Colour:	Browns, blue and green
Issued:	1985 - 1985

Beswick Number	Price			
	U.S. $	Can. $	U.K. £	Aust. $
SS4	125.00	175.00	80.00	200.00

SS11
MRS. TIGGY-WINKLE™

Designer:	Harry Sales
Modeller:	Graham Tongue
Height:	5", 12.7 cm
Colour:	Browns, green, white and blue
Issued:	1985 - 1985

Beswick Number	Price			
	U.S. $	Can. $	U.K. £	Aust. $
SS11	125.00	175.00	80.00	200.00

SS26
YOCK YOCK™
(In The Tub)

Designer:	Harry Sales
Modeller:	David Lyttleton
Height:	2", 5.0 cm
Colour:	Pink and brown
Issued:	1986 - 1986

Beswick Number	Price			
	U.S. $	Can. $	U.K. £	Aust. $
SS26	350.00	475.00	225.00	450.00

SS27
PETER RABBIT™
(In The Watering Can)

Designer: Harry Sales
Modeller: David Lyttleton
Height: 3 ¼", 8.3 cm
Colour: Browns and blue
Issued: 1986 - 1986

| Beswick | Price | | | |
Number	U.S. $	Can. $	U.K. £	Aust. $
SS27	450.00	500.00	300.00	450.00

BEDTIME CHORUS

1801
PIANIST™

Designer:	Albert Hallam
Height:	3", 7.6 cm
Colour:	Pale blue and yellow
Issued:	1962 - 1969

Beswick	Price			
Number	U.S. $	Can. $	U.K. £	Aust. $
1801	175.00	275.00	125.00	250.00

1802
PIANO™

Designer:	Albert Hallam
Height:	3", 7.6 cm
Colour:	Brown and white
Issued:	1962 - 1969

Beswick	Price			
Number	U.S. $	Can. $	U.K. £	Aust. $
1802	115.00	175.00	75.00	175.00

1803
CAT - SINGING™

Designer:	Albert Hallam
Height:	1 ¼", 3.2 cm
Colour:	Ginger stripe
Issued:	1962 - 1971

Beswick	Price			
Number	U.S. $	Can. $	U.K. £	Aust. $
1803	85.00	135.00	50.00	135.00

1804
BOY WITHOUT SPECTACLES™

Designer:	Albert Hallam
Height:	3 ½", 8.9 cm
Colour:	Yellow, white and blue
Issued:	1962 - 1969

Beswick Number	Price			
	U.S. $	Can. $	U.K. £	Aust. $
1804	225.00	350.00	150.00	350.00

1805
BOY WITH SPECTACLES™

Designer:	Albert Hallam
Height:	3", 7.6 cm
Colour:	Green, white and blue
Issued:	1962 - 1969

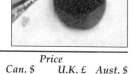

Beswick Number	Price			
	U.S. $	Can. $	U.K. £	Aust. $
1805	225.00	350.00	150.00	350.00

1824
DOG - SINGING™

Designer:	Albert Hallam
Height:	1 ½", 3.8 cm
Colour:	Tan
Issued:	1962 - 1971

Beswick Number	Price			
	U.S. $	Can. $	U.K. £	Aust. $
1824	100.00	150.00	65.00	150.00

1825
BOY WITH GUITAR™

Designer:	Albert Hallam
Height:	3", 7.6 cm
Colour:	Blue-grey, brown and blue
Issued:	1962 - 1969

Beswick		Price		
Number	U.S. $	Can. $	U.K. £	Aust. $
1825	225.00	350.00	150.00	350.00

1826
GIRL WITH HARP™

Designer:	Albert Hallam
Height:	3 ½", 8.9 cm
Colour:	Purple, red and brown
Issued:	1962 - 1969

Beswick		Price		
Number	U.S. $	Can. $	U.K. £	Aust. $
1826	225.00	350.00	150.00	350.00

BESWICK BEARS

BB001
WILLIAM™

Designer: Unknown
Height: 2 ¼", 5.7 cm
Colour: Brown bear, blue apron,
white and rose book
Issued: 1993 - 1993

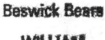

Beswick	Price			
Number	U.S. $	Can. $	U.K. £	Aust. $
BB001	100.00	150.00	65.00	150.00

BB002
BILLY™

Designer: Unknown
Height: 4", 10.1 cm
Colour: Brown bear, green waistcoat,
blue hat, yellow, red and blue ball
Issued: 1993 - 1993

Beswick	Price			
Number	U.S. $	Can. $	U.K. £	Aust. $
BB002	75.00	100.00	45.00	100.00

BB003
HARRY™

Designer: Unknown
Height: 3 ¼", 8.3 cm
Colour: Brown bear, blue waistcoat,
brown hat, white plates
Issued: 1993 - 1993

Beswick	Price			
Number	U.S. $	Can. $	U.K. £	Aust. $
BB003	75.00	100.00	45.00	100.00

BB004
BOBBY™

Designer:	Unknown
Height:	4", 10.1 cm
Colour:	Brown bear, blue waistcoat, brown hat, yellow ball, black and red bat
Issued:	1993 - 1993

BOBBY hits his ball in the air, It comes to land, he knows not where. *Beswick Bears* BB004

Beswick Number	Price			
	U.S. $	Can. $	U.K. £	Aust. $
BB004	75.00	100.00	45.00	100.00

BB005
JAMES™

Designer:	Unknown
Height:	3 ¾", 9.5 cm
Colour:	Brown bear, yellow waistcoat, blue hat, blue parcel with pink ribbon
Issued:	1993 - 1993

JAMES has a gift wrapped up in a bow – It's a nice little "thank you", un petit cadeau. *Beswick Bears* BB005

Beswick Number	Price			
	U.S. $	Can. $	U.K. £	Aust. $
BB005	75.00	100.00	45.00	100.00

BB006
SUSIE™

Designer:	Unknown
Height:	3 ½", 8.9 cm
Colour:	Brown bear, blue dress, brown recorder
Issued:	1993 - 1993

SUSIE is playing her new recorder Any time she'll play to order. *Beswick Bears* BB006

Beswick Number	Price			
	U.S. $	Can. $	U.K. £	Aust. $
BB006	75.00	100.00	45.00	100.00

BB007
ANGELA™

Designer:	Unknown
Height:	3 ¼", 8.3 cm
Colour:	Brown bear, yellow dress, white flowers
Issued:	1993 - 1993

ANGELA
kneels to pick some flowers
Happily dreaming for
hours and hours.
Beswick Bears
BB007

Beswick Number	Price			
	U.S. $	Can. $	U.K. £	Aust. $
BB007	75.00	100.00	45.00	100.00

BB008
CHARLOTTE™

Designer:	Unknown
Height:	4", 10.1 cm
Colour:	Brown bear, pink dress, blue and yellow parasol
Issued:	1993 - 1993

CHARLOTTE
tries to keep in the shade.
Twirling her parasol,
a pretty young maid.
Beswick Bears
BB008

Beswick Number	Price			
	U.S. $	Can. $	U.K. £	Aust. $
BB008	75.00	100.00	45.00	100.00

BB009
SAM™

Designer:	Unknown
Height:	3 ½", 8.9 cm
Colour:	Brown bear, rose waistcoat, yellow banjo
Issued:	1993 - 1993

SAM
plays his banjo all day long.
Amusing friends
with a tune and a song.
Beswick Bears
BB009

Beswick Number	Price			
	U.S. $	Can. $	U.K. £	Aust. $
BB009	75.00	100.00	45.00	100.00

BB010
LIZZY™

Designer:	Unknown
Height:	2 ¼", 5.7 cm
Colour:	Brown bear, pink dress, paint box
Issued:	1993 - 1993

Beswick *Number*	*Price*			
	U.S. $	*Can. $*	*U.K. £*	*Aust. $*
BB010	75.00	100.00	45.00	100.00

BB011
EMILY™

Designer:	Unknown
Height:	3 ½", 8.9 cm
Colour:	Brown bear, pale blue dress, brown picnic hamper
Issued:	1993 - 1993

Beswick *Number*	*Price*			
	U.S. $	*Can. $*	*U.K. £*	*Aust. $*
BB011	75.00	100.00	45.00	100.00

BB012
SARAH™

Designer:	Unknown
Height:	3 ¼", 8.3 cm
Colour:	Brown bear, green dress, white cup and saucer
Issued:	1993 - 1993

Beswick *Number*	*Price*			
	U.S. $	*Can. $*	*U.K. £*	*Aust. $*
BB012	75.00	100.00	45.00	100.00

JILL BARKLEM'S
BRAMBLY HEDGE

DBH1
POPPY EYEBRIGHT™

Designer:	Harry Sales
Modeller:	David Lyttleton
Height:	3 ¼", 8.3 cm
Colour:	Grey-white and pink dress, white apron trimmed with blue flowers
Issued:	1983 - 1997

Doulton	Price			
Number	U.S. $	Can. $	U.K. £	Aust. $
DBH1	75.00	100.00	35.00	100.00

DBH2
MR. APPLE™

Designer:	Harry Sales
Modeller:	David Lyttleton
Height:	3 ¼", 8.3 cm
Colour:	Black trousers, white and blue striped shirt, white apron
Issued:	1983 - 1997

Doulton	Price			
Number	U.S. $	Can. $	U.K. £	Aust. $
DBH2	85.00	125.00	35.00	125.00

DBH3
MRS. APPLE™

Designer:	Harry Sales
Modeller:	David Lyttleton
Height:	3 ¼", 8.3 cm
Colour:	White and blue striped dress, white apron
Issued:	1983 - 1997

Doulton	Price			
Number	U.S. $	Can. $	U.K. £	Aust. $
DBH3	90.00	125.00	40.00	125.00

DBH4
LORD WOODMOUSE™
Style One

Designer:	Harry Sales
Modeller:	David Lyttleton
Height:	3 ¼", 8.3 cm
Colour:	Green trousers, brown coat and burgundy waistcoat
Issued:	1983 - 1997

Doulton Number	Price			
	U.S. $	Can. $	U.K. £	Aust. $
DBH4	75.00	100.00	35.00	100.00

DBH5
LADY WOODMOUSE™
Style One

Designer:	Harry Sales
Modeller:	David Lyttleton
Height:	3 ¼", 8.3 cm
Colour:	Red and white striped dress, white apron
Issued:	1983 - 1997

Doulton Number	Price			
	U.S. $	Can. $	U.K. £	Aust. $
DBH5	75.00	100.00	35.00	100.00

DBH6
DUSTY DOGWOOD™

Designer:	Harry Sales
Modeller:	David Lyttleton
Height:	3 ¼", 8.3 cm
Colour:	Dark grey suit, red waistcoat
Issued:	1984 - 1995

Doulton Number	Price			
	U.S. $	Can. $	U.K. £	Aust. $
DBH6	90.00	125.00	35.00	125.00

DBH7
WILFRED TOADFLAX™

Designer:	Harry Sales
Modeller:	David Lyttleton
Height:	3 ¼", 8.3 cm
Colour:	Grey trousers, red and white striped shirt
Issued:	1983 - 1997

Royal Doulton
WILFRED TOADFLAX
D BH 7
FROM THE BRAMBLY HEDGE
GIFT COLLECTION
© JILL BARKLEM 1982

Doulton Number	Price			
	U.S. $	Can. $	U.K. £	Aust. $
DBH7	75.00	100.00	35.00	100.00

DBH8
PRIMROSE WOODMOUSE™

Designer:	Harry Sales
Modeller:	David Lyttleton
Height:	3 ¼", 8.3 cm
Colour:	Yellow dress with white apron
Issued:	1983 - 1997

Royal Doulton
PRIMROSE WOODMOUSE
B BH 8
FROM THE BRAMBLY HEDGE
GIFT COLLECTION
© JILL BARKLEM 1982

Doulton Number	Price			
	U.S. $	Can. $	U.K. £	Aust. $
DBH8	75.00	100.00	35.00	100.00

DBH9
OLD MRS. EYEBRIGHT™

Designer:	Harry Sales
Modeller:	David Lyttleton
Height:	3 ¼", 8.3 cm
Colour:	Mauve skirt, white and pink striped shawl, white apron
Issued:	1984 - 1995

Royal Doulton
OLD MRS EYEBRIGHT
D BH 9
FROM THE BRAMBLY HEDGE
GIFT COLLECTION
© JILL BARKLEM 1983

Doulton Number	Price			
	U.S. $	Can. $	U.K. £	Aust. $
DBH9	150.00	200.00	75.00	200.00

DBH10A
MR. TOADFLAX™
First Version (Tail at front, with cushion)

Designer:	Harry Sales
Modeller:	David Lyttleton
Height:	3 ¼", 8.3 cm
Colour:	Blue and white striped shirt, pink trousers, burgundy braces, multicoloured patchwork quilt
Issued:	1984 - 1984

Doulton Number	Price			
	U.S. $	Can. $	U.K. £	Aust. $
DBH10A	2,000.00	2,750.00	1,250.00	2,750.00

DBH10B
MR. TOADFLAX™
Second Version (Tail at back, without cushion)

Designer:	Harry Sales
Modeller:	David Lyttleton
Height:	3 ¼", 8.3 cm
Colour:	Blue and white striped shirt, pink trousers, burgundy braces
Issued:	1984 - 1985

Doulton Number	Price			
	U.S. $	Can. $	U.K. £	Aust. $
DBH10B	600.00	800.00	400.00	800.00

DBH10C
MR. TOADFLAX™
Third Version (Tail at back, with cushion)

Designer:	Harry Sales
Modeller:	David Lyttleton
Height:	3 ¼", 8.3 cm
Colour:	Blue and white striped shirt, lilac trousers, burgundy braces, multicoloured patchwork cushion
Issued:	1985 - 1997

Doulton Number	Price			
	U.S. $	Can. $	U.K. £	Aust. $
DBH10C	85.00	125.00	40.00	125.00

Note: For further illustrations see page 110.

DBH11
MRS. TOADFLAX™

Designer:	Harry Sales
Modeller:	David Lyttleton
Height:	3 ¼", 8.3 cm
Colour:	Green and white striped dress, white apron
Issued:	1985 - 1995

| Doulton Number | Price | | | |
	U.S. $	Can. $	U.K. £	Aust. $
DBH11	95.00	125.00	60.00	125.00

Note: The contents of the bowl may vary in colour.

DBH12
CATKIN™

Designer:	Harry Sales
Modeller:	David Lyttleton
Height:	3 ¼", 8.3 cm
Colour:	Yellow dress and white apron
Issued:	1985 - 1994

| Doulton Number | Price | | | |
	U.S. $	Can. $	U.K. £	Aust. $
DBH12	175.00	225.00	125.00	225.00

DBH13
OLD VOLE™

Designer:	Harry Sales
Modeller:	David Lyttleton
Height:	3 ¼", 8.3 cm
Colour:	Green jacket, blue trousers, yellow waistcoat
Issued:	1985 - 1992

| Doulton Number | Price | | | |
	U.S. $	Can. $	U.K. £	Aust. $
DBH13	375.00	500.00	250.00	500.00

DBH14
BASIL™

Designer:	Harry Sales
Modeller:	David Lyttleton
Height:	3 ¼", 8.3 cm
Colour:	Brown waistcoat, green and white striped trousers
Issued:	1985 - 1992

Doulton Number	Price			
	U.S. $	Can. $	U.K. £	Aust. $
DBH14	350.00	475.00	225.00	475.00

DBH15
MRS. CRUSTYBREAD™

Designer:	Graham Tongue
Modeller:	Ted Chawner
Height:	3 ¼", 8.3 cm
Colour:	Yellow dress, white apron and cap
Issued:	1987 - 1994

Doulton Number	Price			
	U.S. $	Can. $	U.K. £	Aust. $
DBH15	325.00	450.00	200.00	450.00

DBH16
CLOVER™

Designer:	Graham Tongue
Modeller:	Graham Tongue
Height:	3 ¼", 8.3 cm
Colour:	Burgundy dress, white apron
Issued:	1987 - 1997

Doulton Number	Price			
	U.S. $	Can. $	U.K. £	Aust. $
DBH16	65.00	85.00	35.00	85.00

DBH17
TEASEL™

Designer:	Graham Tongue
Modeller:	Ted Chawner
Height:	3 ¼", 8.3 cm
Colour:	Blue-grey dungarees, blue and white striped shirt
Issued:	1987 - 1992

Royal Doulton®
TEASEL
D B H 17
FROM THE BRAMBLY HEDGE
GIFT COLLECTION
© 1987 JILL BARKLEM

Doulton Number	Price			
	U.S. $	Can. $	U.K. £	Aust. $
DBH17	425.00	575.00	200.00	575.00

DBH18
STORE STUMP MONEY BOX™

Designer:	Martyn Alcock
Height:	3 ¼", 8.3 cm
Colour:	Browns
Issued:	1987 - 1989

Royal Doulton®
STORE STUMP MONEY BOX
D B H 18
FROM THE BRAMBLY HEDGE
GIFT COLLECTION
© 1987 JILL BARKLEM

Doulton Number	Price			
	U.S. $	Can. $	U.K. £	Aust. $
DBH18	350.00	475.00	225.00	475.00

DBH19
LILY WEAVER™

Designer:	Graham Tongue
Modeller:	Ted Chawner
Height:	3 ¼", 8.3 cm
Colour:	White dress with green and mauve, white cap
Issued:	1988 - 1993

Royal Doulton®
LILY WEAVER
D B H 19
FROM THE BRAMBLY HEDGE
GIFT COLLECTION
© 1988 JILL BARKLEM

Doulton Number	Price			
	U.S. $	Can. $	U.K. £	Aust. $
DBH19	350.00	475.00	200.00	475.00

DBH20
FLAX WEAVER™

Designer:	Graham Tongue
Modeller:	Ted Chawner
Height:	3 ¼", 8.3 cm
Colour:	Grey trousers, grey and white striped shirt
Issued:	1988 - 1993

Doulton Number	Price			
	U.S. $	Can. $	U.K. £	Aust. $
DBH20	350.00	475.00	200.00	475.00

DBH21
CONKER™

Designer:	Graham Tongue
Modeller:	Ted Chawner
Height:	3 ¼", 8.3 cm
Colour:	Green jacket, yellow waistcoat, green striped trousers
Issued:	1988 - 1994

Doulton Number	Price			
	U.S. $	Can. $	U.K. £	Aust. $
DBH21	350.00	475.00	225.00	475.00

DBH22
PRIMROSE ENTERTAINS™

Designer:	Graham Tongue
Modeller:	Alan Maslankowski
Height:	3 ¼", 8.3 cm
Colour:	Green and yellow dress
Issued:	1990 - 1995

Doulton Number	Price			
	U.S. $	Can. $	U.K. £	Aust. $
DBH22	125.00	175.00	80.00	175.00

DBH23
WILFRED ENTERTAINS™

Designer:	Graham Tongue
Modeller:	Alan Maslankowski
Height:	3 ¼", 8.3 cm
Colour:	Burgundy and yellow outfit, black hat
Issued:	1990 - 1995

Doulton Number	Price			
	U.S. $	Can. $	U.K. £	Aust $
DBH23	125.00	175.00	80.00	175.00

DBH24
MR. SALTAPPLE™

Designer:	Graham Tongue
Modeller:	Warren Platt
Height:	3 ¼", 8.3 cm
Colour:	Blue and white striped outfit, beige base
Issued:	1993 - 1997

Doulton Number	Price			
	U.S. $	Can. $	U.K. £	Aust. $
DBH24	75.00	100.00	40.00	100.00

DBH25
MRS. SALTAPPLE™

Designer:	Graham Tongue
Modeller:	Warren Platt
Height:	3 ¼", 8.3 cm
Colour:	Rose and cream dress, beige hat and base
Issued:	1993 - 1997

Doulton Number	Price			
	U.S. $	Can. $	U.K. £	Aust. $
DBH25	75.00	100.00	40.00	100.00

DBH26
DUSTY AND BABY™

Designer:	Graham Tongue
Modeller:	Martyn Alcock
Height:	3 ¾", 9.5 cm
Colour:	Dusty: Blue striped shirt with beige dungarees
	Baby: White gown
Issued:	1995 - 1997

Doulton Number	Price			
	U.S. $	Can. $	U.K. £	Aust. $
DBH26	85.00	125.00	40.00	125.00

DBH30
THE ICE BALL™

Designer:	Shane Ridge
Modeller:	Shane Ridge
Height:	4 ¼", 10.8 cm
Colour:	Green, yellow, pink and white
Issued:	2000 in a limited edition of 3,000

Doulton Number	Price			
	U.S. $	Can. $	U.K. £	Aust. $
DBH30	—	—	120.00	—

DBH31
LORD WOODMOUSE™
Style Two

Designer:	Shane Ridge
Modeller:	Shane Ridge
Height:	4 ¼", 10.8 cm
Colour:	Brown, salmon, black, red and yellow
Issued:	2000 to the present

Doulton Number	Price			
	U.S. $	Can. $	U.K. £	Aust. $
DBH31	80.00	—	40.00	—

DBH32
LADY WOODMOUSE™
Style Two

Designer:	Warren Platt
Modeller:	Warren Platt
Height:	4 ¼", 10.8 cm
Colour:	White, pale blue, red and yellow
Issued:	2000 to the present

Doulton	Price			
Number	U.S. $	Can. $	U.K. £	Aust. $
DBH32	80.00	—	40.00	—

DBH33
PRIMROSE PICKING BERRIES™

Designer:	Shane Ridge
Modeller:	Shane Ridge
Height:	3 ½", 8.9 cm
Colour:	Yellow, white and purple
Issued:	2000 to the present

Doulton	Price			
Number	U.S. $	Can. $	U.K. £	Aust. $
DBH33	60.00	—	30.00	—

DBH34
WILFRED CARRIES THE PICNIC™

Designer:	Shane Ridge
Modeller:	Shane Ridge
Height:	3 ½", 8.9 cm
Colour:	Blue, brown and red
Issued:	2000 to the present

Doulton	Price			
Number	U.S. $	Can. $	U.K. £	Aust. $
DBH34	60.00	—	30.00	—

DBH35
WILFRED AND THE TOY CHEST
MONEY BOX™

Designer:	Martyn Alcock
Modeller:	Martyn Alcock
Height:	3 ¾", 9.5 cm
Colour:	Green, yellow, red and black
Issued:	2000 to the present

Doulton Number	Price			
	U.S. $	*Can. $*	*U.K. £*	*Aust. $*
DBH35	120.00	—	80.00	—

Mr. Toadflax
front view

Third Version —Tail at the Back   First Version — Tail at the Front   Second Version — Tail at the Back
With Cushion   Without Cushion

Mr. Toadflax
back view

Third Version — With Cushion   First Version — With Cushion   Second Version — Without Cushion

THE CAT'S CHORUS

CC1
PURRFECT PITCH™

Modeller:	Shane Ridge
Height:	4", 10.1 cm
Colour:	White cat, black dress, red gloves and shoes, black hair
Issued:	1998 to the present

Beswick Number	Price			
	U.S. $	Can. $	U.K. £	Aust. $
CC1	—	—	27.00	—

CC2
CALYPSO KITTEN™

Modeller:	Shane Ridge
Height:	4", 10.1 cm
Colour:	Black cat, patterned yellow shirt, beige trousers, red and yellow drum
Issued:	1998 to the present

Beswick Number	Price			
	U.S. $	Can. $	U.K. £	Aust. $
CC2	—	—	27.00	—

CC3
ONE COOL CAT™

Modeller:	Shane Ridge
Height:	4", 10.1 cm
Colour:	Ginger cat, blue suit with black lapels, cuffs and pockets, white shirt, black shoes, yellow saxophone
Issued:	1998 to the present

Beswick Number	Price			
	U.S. $	Can. $	U.K. £	Aust. $
CC3	—	—	27.00	—

CC4
RATCATCHER BILK

Modeller:	Shane Ridge
Height:	4", 10.1 cm
Colour:	White cat, blue shirt and hat, yellow waistcoat, black trousers and clarinet
Issued:	1998 to the present

Beswick Number	Price			
	U.S. $	Can. $	U.K. £	Aust. $
CC4	—	—	27.00	—

CC5
TRAD JAZZ TOM™

Modeller:	Shane Ridge
Height:	4", 10.1 cm
Colour:	Grey cat, trousers and waistcoat, lemon shirt, black hat, yellow trumpet
Issued:	1998 to the present

Beswick Number	Price			
	U.S. $	Can. $	U.K. £	Aust. $
CC5	—	—	27.00	—

CC6
CATWALKING BASS™

Modeller:	Shane Ridge
Height:	4", 10.1 cm
Colour:	White cat, yellow jacket, green shirt, red trousers, black hat, tan bass
Issued:	1998 to the present

Beswick Number	Price			
	U.S. $	Can. $	U.K. £	Aust. $
CC6	—	—	27.00	—

CC7
FELINE FLAMENCO™

Modeller: Shane Ridge
Height: 4", 10.1 cm
Colour: Ginger cat, lemon shirt, black waistcoat
           and trousers, red and white cumberbund,
           tan guitar
Issued: 1998 to the present

| Beswick | Price | | | |
Number	U.S. $	Can. $	U.K. £	Aust. $
CC7	—	—	27.00	—

CC8
BRAVURA BRASS™

Modeller: Shane Ridge
Height: 4", 10.1 cm
Colour: Ginger cat, black suit and shoes,
           white shirt, yellow french horn
Issued: 1998 to the present

| Beswick | Price | | | |
Number	U.S. $	Can. $	U.K. £	Aust. $
CC8	—	—	27.00	—

CC9
FAT CAT™

Modeller: Shane Ridge
Height: 3 ¾", 9.5 cm
Colour: Brown, yellow and blue
Issued: 1999 to the present

| Beswick | Price | | | |
Number	U.S. $	Can. $	U.K. £	Aust. $
CC9	—	—	40.00	—

CC10
GLAM GUITAR™

Modeller:	Shane Ridge
Height:	4 ¼", 10.8 cm
Colour:	Red, yellow and white
Issued:	1999 to the present

Beswick	Price			
Number	U.S. $	Can. $	U.K. £	Aust. $
CC10	—	—	27.00	—

COMPTON & WOODHOUSE

ARCHIE

Designer:	Unknown
Height:	4 ½", 11.9 cm
Colour:	Brown bear with light blue waistcoat and red and white spotted handkerchief
Issued:	1997 to the present
Series:	The Beswick Bears Collection

Beswick Number	Price			
	U.S. $	Can. $	U.K. £	Aust. $
—	85.00	125.00	50.00	125.00

BENJAMIN

Designer:	Unknown
Height:	4 ½", 11.9 cm
Colour:	Brown bear wearing a bright yellow scarf
Issued:	1996 to the present
Series:	The Beswick Bears Collection

Beswick Number	Price			
	U.S. $	Can. $	U .K. £	Aust. $
—	85.00	125.00	50.00	125.00

BERTIE

Designer:	Unknown
Height:	4 ½", 11.9 cm
Colour:	Dark brown bear, light brown straw hat with red and purple band, yellow cane
Issued:	1997 to the present
Series:	The Beswick Bears Collection

Beswick Number	Price			
	U.S. $	Can. $	U.K. £	Aust. $
—	85.00	125.00	50.00	125.00

HENRY

Designer:	Unknown
Height:	4 ½", 11.9 cm
Colour:	Dark brown bear, purple tie, brown briefcase
Issued:	1998 to the present
Series:	The Beswick Bears Collection

Beswick Number	Price			
	U.S. $	Can. $	U.K. £	Aust. $
—	85.00	125.00	50.00	125.00

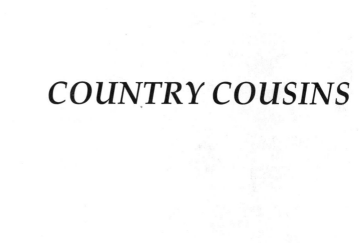

COUNTRY COUSINS

PM 2101
SWEET SUZIE
Thank You

Designer:	Unknown
Height:	2 ¾", 7.0 cm
Colour:	Brown rabbit wearing a brown and yellow pinafore
Issued:	1994 - 1994

Back Stamp	Beswick Number	Price			
		U.S. $	Can. $	U.K. £	Aust. $
BK-1	PM2101	35.00	50.00	20.00	55.00

PM 2102
PETER
Once Upon A Time

Designer:	Unknown
Height:	2 ½", 5.6 cm
Colour:	Brown hedgehog wearing a blue suit and a white bowtie
Issued:	1994 - 1994

Back Stamp	Beswick Number	Price			
		U.S. $	Can. $	U.K. £	Aust. $
BK-1	PM2102	35.00	50.00	20.00	55.00

PM 2103
HARRY
A New Home for Fred

Designer:	Unknown
Height:	2", 5.0 cm
Colour:	Brown hedgehog wearing a blue and white jumper and brown trousers
Issued:	1994 - 1994

Back Stamp	Beswick Number	Price			
		U.S. $	Can. $	U.K. £	Aust. $
BK-1	PM2103	35.00	50.00	20.00	55.00

PM 2104
MICHAEL
Happily Ever After

Designer:	Unknown
Height:	2 ½", 6.4 cm
Colour:	Brown rabbit wearing a green jacket
Issued:	1994 - 1994

Back Stamp	Beswick Number	Price			
		U.S. $	Can. $	U.K. £	Aust. $
BK-1	PM2104	35.00	50.00	20.00	55.00

PM 2105
BERTRAM
Ten Out of Ten

Designer:	Unknown
Height:	3", 7.6 cm
Colour:	Brown owl wearing a green and blue striped waistcoat, a red bow tie and blue mortar board with red tassel
Issued:	1994 - 1994

Back Stamp	Beswick Number	Price			
		U.S. $	Can. $	U.K. £	Aust. $
BK-1	PM2105	35.00	50.00	20.00	55.00

PM 2106
LEONARDO
Practice Makes Perfect

Designer:	Unknown
Height:	2 ¾", 7.0 cm
Colour:	Brown owl wearing a brown hat, white palette and blue paintbrush
Issued:	1994 - 1994

Back Stamp	Beswick Number	Price			
		U.S. $	Can. $	U.K. £	Aust. $
BK-1	PM2106	35.00	50.00	20.00	55.00

PM 2107
LILY
Flowers Picked Just for You

Designer:	Unknown
Height:	3", 7.6 cm
Colour:	Brown hedgehog wearing a pink dress with matching bonnet with white ribbon, yellow pinafore with white collar
Issued:	1994 - 1994

Back Stamp	Beswick Number	Price			
		U.S. $	Can. $	U.K. £	Aust. $
BK-1	PM2107	35.00	50.00	20.00	55.00

PM 2108
PATRICK
This Way's Best

Designer:	Unknown
Height:	3", 7.6 cm
Colour:	Brown owl wearing a blue and yellow checked waistcoat, white collar and blue bow tie, yellow hat with red band
Issued:	1994 - 1994

Back Stamp	Beswick Number	Price			
		U.S. $	Can. $	U.K. £	Aust. $
BK-1	PM2108	35.00	50.00	20.00	55.00

PM 2109
JAMIE
Hurrying Home

Designer:	Unknown
Height:	3", 7.6 cm
Colour:	Brown hedgehog wearing a pink sailor top with white stripes, blue trousers
Issued:	1994 - 1994

Back Stamp	Beswick Number	Price			
		U.S. $	Can. $	U.K. £	Aust. $
BK-1	PM2109	35.00	50.00	20.00	55.00

PM 2111
MUM AND LIZZIE
Let's Get Busy

Designer:	Unknown
Height:	3 ¼", 8.3 cm
Colour:	Large brown rabbit wearing a blue dress and white pinafore
	Small brown rabbit wearing a white pinafore
Issued:	1994 - 1994

Back Stamp	Beswick Number	Price			
		U.S. $	Can. $	U.K. £	Aust. $
BK-1	PM2111	50.00	75.00	30.00	65.00

PM 2112
MOLLY AND TIMMY
Picnic Time

Designer:	Unknown
Height:	2 ¾", 7 cm
Colour:	Large brown mouse wearing a pink dress, blue pinafore, yellow bonnet
	Small brown mouse wearing yellow dungarees, white top, blue hat, carrying a brown teddy bear
Issued:	1994 - 1994

Back Stamp	Beswick Number	Price			
		U.S. $	Can. $	U.K. £	Aust. $
BK-1	PM2112	50.00	75.00	30.00	65.00

PM 2113
POLLY AND SARAH
Good News!

Designer:	Unknown
Height:	3 ¼", 8.3 cm
Colour:	Brown rabbit wearing a blue dress and a pink apron
	Brown hedgehog wearing a blue dress and scarf, green jacket and a white pinafore
Issued:	1994 - 1994

Back Stamp	Beswick Number	Price			
		U.S. $	Can. $	U.K. £	Aust. $
BK-1	PM2113	50.00	75.00	30.00	65.00

PM 2114
BILL AND TED
Working Together

Designer:	Unknown
Height:	3 ¼", 8.3 cm
Colour:	Brown mouse in blue dungarees
	Brown hedgehog in green dungarees
Issued:	1994 - 1994

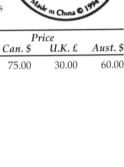

Back Stamp	Beswick Number	Price			
		U.S. $	Can. $	U.K. £	Aust. $
BK-1	PM2114	50.00	75.00	30.00	60.00

PM 2115
JACK AND DAISY
How Does Your Garden Grow?

Designer:	Unknown
Height:	2 ¾", 7 cm
Colour:	Male - brown mouse, white shirt, blue dungarees
	Female - brown mouse, pink and white striped dress, white pinafore
Issued:	1994 - 1994

Back Stamp	Beswick Number	Price			
		U.S. $	Can. $	U.K. £	Aust. $
BK-1	PM2115	50.00	75.00	30.00	60.00

PM 2116
ALISON AND DEBBIE
Friendship is Fun

Designer:	Unknown
Height:	2 ¾", 7 cm
Colour:	Rabbit - brown, pink dress, white pinafore
	Squirrel - brown, blue dress, pink apron
Issued:	1994 - 1994

Back Stamp	Beswick Number	Price			
		U.S. $	Can. $	U.K. £	Aust. $
BK-1	PM2116	50.00	75.00	30.00	60.00

PM 2119
ROBERT AND ROSIE
Perfect Partners

Designer:	Unknown
Height:	3 ¼", 8.3 cm
Colour:	Male - brown squirrel, blue dungarees, blue hat with red band Female - brown squirrel, pink dress with white collar, yellow hat
Issued:	1994 - 1994

Back Stamp	Beswick Number	Price			
		U.S. $	Can. $	U.K. £	Aust. $
BK-1	PM2119	50.00	75.00	30.00	60.00

PM 2120
SAMMY
Treasure Hunting

Designer:	Unknown
Height:	2 ¼", 5.7 cm
Colour:	Brown squirrel wearing a green shirt, blue sack
Issued:	1994 - 1994

Back Stamp	Beswick Number	Price			
		U.S. $	Can. $	U.K. £	Aust. $
BK-1	PM2120	35.00	50.00	20.00	55.00

DAVID HAND'S
ANIMALAND

1148
DINKUM PLATYPUS™

Designer:	Arthur Gredington
Height:	4 ¼", 10.8 cm
Colour:	Brown and beige platypus, green base
Issued:	1949 - 1955

Beswick Number	Price			
	U.S. $	Can. $	U.K. £	Aust. $
1148	250.00	350.00	150.00	325.00

1150
ZIMMY LION™

Designer:	Arthur Gredington
Height:	3 ¾", 9.5 cm
Colour:	Brown lion with white face
Issued:	1949 - 1955

Beswick Number	Price			
	U.S. $	Can. $	U.K. £	Aust. $
1150	575.00	750.00	350.00	750.00

1151
FELIA™

Designer:	Arthur Gredington
Height:	4", 10.1 cm
Colour:	Green cat
Issued:	1949 - 1955

Beswick Number	Price			
	U.S. $	Can. $	U.K. £	Aust. $
1151	750.00	1,100.00	425.00	1,000.00

1152
GINGER NUTT™

Designer:	Arthur Gredington
Height:	4", 10.1 cm
Colour:	Brown and beige squirrel, green base
Issued:	1949 - 1955

Beswick Number	Price			
	U.S. $	Can. $	U.K. £	Aust. $
1152	775.00	1,100.00	475.00	1,100.00

1153
HAZEL NUTT™

Designer:	Arthur Gredington
Height:	3 ¾", 9.5 cm
Colour:	Brown and beige squirrel, green base
Issued:	1949 - 1955

Beswick Number	Price			
	U.S. $	Can. $	U.K. £	Aust. $
1153	775.00	1,100.00	475.00	1,100.00

1154
OSCAR OSTRICH™

Designer:	Arthur Gredington
Height:	3 ¾", 9.5 cm
Colour:	Beige and mauve ostrich, brown base
Issued:	1949 - 1955

Beswick Number	Price			
	U.S. $	Can. $	U.K. £	Aust. $
1154	775.00	1,100.00	475.00	1,100.00

1155
DUSTY MOLE™

Designer:	Arthur Gredington
Height:	3 ½", 8.9 cm
Colour:	Blue mole, white face
Issued:	1949 - 1955

| Beswick | | Price | | |
Number	U.S. $	Can. $	U.K. £	Aust. $
1155	450.00	600.00	275.00	550.00

1156
LOOPY HARE™

Designer:	Arthur Gredington
Height:	4 ¼", 10.8 cm
Colour:	Brown and beige hare
Issued:	1949 - 1955

| Beswick | | Price | | |
Number	U.S. $	Can. $	U.K. £	Aust. $
1156	675.00	1,000.00	400.00	1,000.00

ENGLISH COUNTRY FOLK

ECF 1
HUNTSMAN FOX™

Designer:	Amanda Hughes-Lubeck
Height:	5 ¾", 14.6 cm
Colour:	Dark green jacket and cap, blue-grey trousers, green wellingtons
Issued:	1993 - 1998

ECF 1
HUNTSMAN FOX

Back Stamp	Beswick Number	Price			
		U.S. $	Can. $	U.K. £	Aust. $
ECF 1	9150	65.00	100.00	40.00	100.00

ECF 2
FISHERMAN OTTER™

Designer:	Warren Platt
Height:	5 ¾", 14.6 cm
Colour:	Yellow shirt and hat, dark green waistcoat, blue-grey trousers, green wellingtons
Issued:	1993 - 1998

ECF 2
FISHERMAN OTTER

Back Stamp	Beswick Number	Price			
		U.S. $	Can. $	U.K. £	Aust. $
ECF 2	9152	65.00	100.00	40.00	100.00

ECF 3
GARDENER RABBIT™
First Variation

Designer:	Warren Platt
Height:	6", 15.0 cm
Colour:	White shirt, red pullover, blue trousers, grey hat, black wellingtons
Issued:	1993 - 1999
Varieties:	ECF 12

ECF 3
GARDENER RABBIT

Back Stamp	Beswick Number	Price			
		U.S. $	Can. $	U.K. £	Aust. $
ECF 3	9155	65.00	100.00	35.00	100.00

ECF 4
GENTLEMAN PIG™
First Variation

Designer:	Amanda Hughes-Lubeck
Height:	5 ¾", 14.6 cm
Colour:	Dark brown suit, yellow waistcoat
Issued:	1993 - 1999
Varieties:	ECF 10

BESWICK
B
ENGLAND
ECF 4
GENTLEMAN PIG

Back Stamp	Beswick Number	Price			
		U.S. $	Can. $	U.K. £	Aust. $
ECF 4	9149	65.00	100.00	35.00	110.00

ECF 5
SHEPHERD SHEEPDOG™

Designer:	Warren Platt
Height:	6 ¾", 17.2 cm
Colour:	Yellow smock
Issued:	1993 - 1999

BESWICK
B
ENGLAND
ECF 5
SHEPHERD SHEEPDOG

Back Stamp	Beswick Number	Price			
		U.S. $	Can. $	U.K. £	Aust. $
ECF 5	9156	65.00	100.00	35.00	110.00

ECF 6
HIKER BADGER™
First Variation

Designer:	Warren Platt
Height:	5 ¼", 13.3 cm
Colour:	Yellow shirt, blue waistcoat, red cap and socks
Issued:	1993 - 1999
Varieties:	ECF 9

BESWICK
B
ENGLAND
ECF 6
HIKER BADGER

Back Stamp	Beswick Number	Price			
		U.S. $	Can. $	U.K. £	Aust. $
ECF 6	9157	65.00	100.00	35.00	110.00

ECF 7
MRS. RABBIT BAKING™
First Variation

Designer:	Martyn Alcock
Height:	5 ½", 14.0 cm
Colour:	Mauve dress, white apron and cap
Issued:	1994 - 1999
Varieties:	ECF 13

ECF 7
MRS RABBIT BAKING

Back Stamp	Beswick Number	Price			
		U.S. $	Can. $	U.K. £	Aust. $
ECF 7	—	65.00	110.00	35.00	110.00

ECF 8
THE LADY PIG™
First Variation

Designer:	Amanda Hughes-Lubeck
Height:	5 ½", 14.0 cm
Colour:	Green jacket, skirt and hat, brown umbrella
Issued:	1995 - 1999
Varieties:	ECF 11

ECF 8
THE LADY PIG

Back Stamp	Beswick Number	Price			
		U.S. $	Can. $	U.K. £	Aust. $
ECF 8	—	65.00	110.00	35.00	110.00

ECF 9
HIKER BADGER™
Second Variation

Designer:	Warren Platt
Height:	5 ¼", 13.3 cm
Colour:	Green shirt and trousers, red jumper, hat and socks, black walking stick
Issued:	1997 in a special edition of 1,000
Varieties:	ECF 6

ECF 9
HIKER BADGER
NEW COLOURWAY 1997
PRODUCED EXCLUSIVELY FOR
20th CENTURY FAIRS JUNE 1997
IN A SPECIAL EDITION OF 1,000
85

Back Stamp	Beswick Number	Price			
		U.S. $	Can. $	U.K. £	Aust. $
ECF 9	9157	125.00	175.00	75.00	175.00

ECF 10
GENTLEMAN PIG™
Second Variation

Designer:	Amanda Hughes-Lubeck
Height:	5 ¾", 14.6 cm
Colour:	Light brown suit and waistcoat
Issued:	1998 in a limited edition of 2,000
Varieties:	ECF 4

Back Stamp	Beswick Number	Price U.S. $	Can. $	U.K. £	Aust. $
ECF 10	9149	75.00	110.00	50.00	110.00

ECF 11
THE LADY PIG™
Second Variation

Designer:	Amanda Hughes-Lubeck
Height:	5 ½", 14.0 cm
Colour:	Brown skirt, jacket and hat, light brown umbrella
Issued:	1998 in a limited edition of 2,000
Varieties:	ECF 8

Back Stamp	Beswick Number	Price U.S. $	Can. $	U.K. £	Aust. $
ECF 11	—	75.00	110.00	50.00	110.00

ECF 12
GARDENER RABBIT™
Second Variation

Designer:	Warren Platt
Height:	6", 15.0 cm
Colour:	Black hat, slate pullover
Issued:	1998 in a limited edition of 2,000
Varieties:	ECF 3

Back Stamp	Beswick Number	Price U.S. $	Can. $	U.K. £	Aust. $
ECF 12	9155	90.00	125.00	60.00	125.00

ECF 13
MRS. RABBIT BAKING™
Second Variation

Designer:	Martyn Alcock
Height:	5 ½", 14.0 cm
Colour:	Grey dress, yellow trimmed apron, rust cap
Issued:	1998 in a limited edition of 2,000
Varieties:	ECF 7

Back Stamp	Beswick Number	Price			
		U.S. $	Can. $	U.K. £	Aust. $
ECF 13	—	90.00	125.00	60.00	125.00

ENID BLYTON'S
NODDY™ COLLECTION

3676
BIG EARS™

Designer:	Enid Blyton
Modeller:	Andy Moss
Height:	5", 12.7 cm
Colour:	Red and white striped shirt, dark blue jacket, yellow buttons and trousers, red hat
Issued:	1997 in a special edition of 1,500

Doulton Number	Price			
	U.S. $	Can. $	U.K. £	Aust. $
3676	85.00	125.00	60.00	135.00

3678
NODDY™

Designer:	Enid Blyton
Modeller	Andy Moss
Height:	5", 12.7 cm
Colour:	Red shirt and shoes, light blue trousers, dark blue hat with light brown bell
Issued:	1997 in a special edition of 1,500

Doulton Number	Price			
	U.S. $	Can. $	U.K. £	Aust. $
3678	85.00	125.00	60.00	135.00

BEDTIME CHORUS™

Boy with Spectacles, Girl with Harp, Cat-Singing, Pianist, Piano, Dog-Singing, Boy without Spectacles, Boy with Guitar

BESWICK BEARS™

James

Sam

Billy

Sarah

Emily

Charlotte

BRAMBLY HEDGE™

Conker

Basil

Clover

Old Mrs. Eyebright

Mrs. Apple

Mrs. Toadflax

Flax Weaver

Mr. Apple

Wilfred Toadflax

BRAMBLY HEDGE™

Catkin

Old Vole

Mrs. Saltapple

Wilfred Entertains

Lady Woodmouse, Style One

Primrose Entertains

Wilfred Carries the Picnic

Primrose Picking Berries

Wilfred and the Toy Chest

COMPTON & WOODHOUSE

Archie

Benjamin

Henry

DAVID HAND'S ANIMALAND™

Felia

Dusty Mole

Hazel Nutt

Loopy Hare

Ginger Nutt

Zimmy Lion

THE PIG PROMENADE™

James the Triangle Player

Benjamin

Thomas

LITTLE LIKEABLES™

Treat Me Gently

On Top of the World

My Pony

ENID BLYTON'S NODDY™ COLLECTION

Noddy

Big Ears

Mr. Plod

COUNTRY COUSINS™

Alison and Debbie
"Friendship is Fun"

Patrick
"This Way's Best"

Polly and Sarah
"Good News!"

Bertram
"Ten Out of Ten"

Mum and Lizzie
"Let's Get Busy"

Molly and Timmy
"Picnic Time"

Lily
"Flowers Picked Just For You"

Jack and Daisy
"How Does Your Garden Grow?"

Bill and Ted
"Working Together"

OLD BEAR™

Don't Worry Rabbit

Welcome Home, Old Bear

The Snowflake Biscuits

Waiting For Snow

Time For Bed

The Long Red Scarf

Time For a Cuddle, Hug Me Tight

Ruff's Prize

Bramwell Brown Has a Good Idea

RUPERT BEAR™

Rupert Bear Snowballing

Algy Pug

Pong Ping

ENGLISH COUNTRY FOLK™

Gentleman Pig, First Variation

Mrs. Rabbit Baking, First Variation

The Lady Pig, First Variation

WIND IN THE WILLOWS™

Ratty

Weasel Gamekeeper

Toad, Style One

3679
MR. PLOD™

Designer:	Enid Blyton
Modeller:	Andy Moss
Height:	5", 12.7 cm
Colour:	Dark blue uniform, yellow buttons, white stripes on cuffs and shoulders, blue helmet with yellow
Issued:	1998 in a special edition of 1,500

Doulton Number	Price			
	U.S. $	Can. $	U.K. £	Aust. $
3679	85.00	125.00	60.00	135.00

3770
TESSIE BEAR™

Designer:	Enid Blyton
Modeller:	Andy Moss
Height:	5", 12.7 cm
Colour:	Yellow bear wearing a pink and green skirt and a pink hat with a white bow
Issued:	1998 in a special edition of 1,500

Doulton Number	Price			
	U.S. $	Can. $	U.K. £	Aust. $
3770	85.00	125.00	60.00	135.00

EXPRESS NEWSPAPERS LTD.
RUPERT BEAR

2694
RUPERT BEAR™
Style One

Designer:	Harry Sales
Height:	4 ¼", 10.8 cm
Colour:	Red sweater, yellow check trousers and scarf
Issued:	1980 - 1986

Beswick Number	Price			
	U.S. $	Can. $	U.K. £	Aust. $
2694	400.00	550.00	250.00	575.00

2710
ALGY PUG™

Designer:	Harry Sales
Height:	4", 10.1 cm
Colour:	Grey jacket, yellow waistcoat, brown trousers
Issued:	1981 - 1986

Beswick Number	Price			
	U.S. $	Can. $	U.K. £	Aust. $
2710	300.00	425.00	200.00	450.00

2711
PONG PING™

Designer:	Harry Sales
Height:	4 ¼", 10.8 cm
Colour:	Dark green jacket, gold trousers
Issued:	1981 - 1986

Beswick Number	Price			
	U.S. $	Can. $	U.K. £	Aust. $
2711	300.00	425.00	200.00	450.00

2720
BILL BADGER™
Style One

Designer:	Harry Sales
Height:	2 ¾", 7.0 cm
Colour:	Dark grey jacket, light grey trousers and red bowtie
Issued:	1981 - 1986

| Beswick | Price | | | |
Number	U.S. $	Can. $	U.K. £	Aust. $
2720	400.00	550.00	250.00	575.00

2779
RUPERT BEAR SNOWBALLING™

Designer:	Harry Sales
Height:	4 ¼", 10.8 cm
Colour:	Red coat, yellow with brown striped trousers and scarf
Issued:	1982 - 1986

| Beswick | Price | | | |
Number	U.S. $	Can. $	U.K. £	Aust. $
2779	500.00	675.00	350.00	675.00

RUPERT BEAR™
Style Two

Designer:	Martyn Alcock
Height:	5 ¾", 14.6 cm
Colour:	Red sweater, yellow check trousers and scarf
Issued:	1998 in a limited edition of 1,920

| Beswick | Price | | | |
Number	U.S. $	Can. $	U.K. £	Aust. $
—	75.00	95.00	40.00	95.00

Note: Issued as one of a pair with Podgy Pig.

PODGY PIG™

Modeller:	Martyn Alcock
Height:	5 ¾", 14.6 cm
Colour:	Brown suit, red scarf, black socks, white shoes
Issued:	1998 in a limited edition of 1,920

Beswick	Price			
Number	U.S. $	Can. $	U.K. £	Aust. $
—	75.00	95.00	40.00	95.00

Note: Issued as one of a pair with Rupert Bear, Style Two.

BILL BADGER™
Style Two

Modeller:	Martyn Alcock
Height:	5", 12.7 cm
Colour:	Turquoise jacket, yellow waistcoat, purple trousers
Issued:	2000 in a limited edition of 1,920

Beswick		Price			
Number		U.S. $	Can. $	U.K. £	Aust. $
—	Pair with Edward Trunk	—	—	90.00	—

Note: Priced as a pair with Edward Trunk.

EDWARD TRUNK™

Modeller:	Martyn Alcock
Height:	5 ¼", 13.3 cm
Colour:	Blue coat, red scarf, yellow check trousers
Issued:	2000 in a limited edition of 1,920

Beswick		Price			
Number		U.S. $	Can. $	U.K. £	Aust. $
—	Pair with Bill Badger (Style Two)	—	—	90.00	—

Note: Priced as a pair with Bill Badger, Style Two.

RUPERT BEAR AND ALGY PUG GO-CARTING™

Modeller:	Martyn Alcock
Height:	4 ¾", 12.1 cm
Colour:	Red, blue, yellow, brown and green
Issued:	2000 in a limited edition of 2,500
Series:	Tableau

Beswick Number	Price			
	U.S. $	Can. $	U.K. £	Aust. $
—	—	—	125.00	—

RUPERT WITH SATCHEL™

Modeller:	Martyn Alcock
Height:	5", 12.7 cm
Colour:	Red sweater, yellow check trousers, white shoes, brown satchel
Issued:	2000 in a limited edition of 2,000

Beswick Number	Price			
	U.S. $	Can. $	U.K. £	Aust. $
—	—	—	45.00	—

FOOTBALLING
FELINES

FF2
MEE-OUCH

Designer:	Andy Moss	
Height:	3 ¼", 8.3 cm	
Colour:	Blue shirt and socks, white shorts, black boots	
Issued:	1998 in a special edition of 1,500	
Series:	Footballing Felines	

Beswick	Price			
Number	U.S. $	Can. $	U.K. £	Aust. $
FF2	75.00	125.00	45.00	125.00

Note: FF1 not issued.

FF3
KITCAT

Designer:	Andy Moss	
Height:	4 ¼", 10.8 cm	
Colour:	Red shirt and socks, white shorts, black boots	
Issued:	1998 in a special edition of 1,500	
Series:	Footballing Felines	

Beswick	Price			
Number	U.S. $	Can. $	U.K. £	Aust. $
FF3	75.00	125.00	45.00	125.00

FF4
DRIBBLE

Designer:	Andy Moss	
Height:	4 ¼", 10.8 cm	
Colour:	White shirt and socks, black shorts and boots	
Issued:	1998 in a special edition of 1,500	
Series:	Footballing Felines	

Beswick	Price			
Number	U.S. $	Can. $	U.K. £	Aust. $
FF4	75.00	125.00	45.00	125.00

FF5
THROW IN

Designer:	Andy Moss
Height:	6", 15.0 cm
Colour:	Yellow shirt and socks, white shorts, black boots
Issued:	1999 in a special edition of 1,500
Series:	Footballing Felines

Beswick	Price			
Number	U.S. $	Can. $	U.K. £	Aust. $
FF5	75.00	125.00	45.00	125.00

FF6
REFFEREE: RED CARD

Designer:	Andy Moss
Height:	6 ¼", 15.9 cm
Colour:	Black uniform; black and white socks
Issued:	1999 in a special edition of 1,500
Series:	Footballing Felines

Beswick	Price			
Number	U.S. $	Can. $	U.K. £	Aust. $
FF6	75.00	125.00	45.00	125.00

HANNA-BARBERA

THE FLINTSTONES
TOP CAT

THE FLINTSTONES
1996-1997

3577
PEBBLES FLINTSTONE™

Designer:	Simon Ward
Height:	3 ½", 8.9 cm
Colour:	Green dress, blue pants, red hair, light brown base
Issued:	1997 in a limited edition of 2,000

Beswick Number	Price			
	U.S. $	Can. $	U.K. £	Aust. $
3577	55.00	80.00	40.00	100.00

3579
BAMM BAMM™

Designer:	Simon Ward
Height:	3", 7.6 cm
Colour:	Light and dark brown pants, white hair, yellow club, light brown base
Issued:	1997 in a limited edition of 2,000

Beswick Number	Price			
	U.S. $	Can. $	U.K. £	Aust. $
3579	55.00	80.00	40.00	100.00

3583
WILMA FLINTSTONE™

Designer:	Simon Ward
Height:	4 ¾", 12.1 cm
Colour:	White dress, red hair, light brown base
Issued:	1996 in a limited edition of 2,000

Beswick Number	Price			
	U.S. $	Can. $	U.K. £	Aust. $
3583	60.00	90.00	45.00	110.00

3584
BETTY RUBBLE™

Designer:	Simon Ward
Height:	4", 10.1 cm
Colour:	Blue dress, black hair, light brown base
Issued:	1996 in a limited edition of 2,000

Beswick Number	Price			
	U.S. $	Can. $	U.K. £	Aust. $
3584	55.00	80.00	40.00	100.00

3587
BARNEY RUBBLE™

Designer:	Simon Ward
Height:	3 ½", 8.9 cm
Colour:	Reddish brown shirt, yellow hair, light brown base
Issued:	1996 in a limited edition of 2,000

Beswick Number	Price			
	U.S. $	Can. $	U.K. £	Aust. $
3587	55.00	80.00	40.00	100.00

3588
FRED FLINTSTONE™

Designer:	Simon Ward
Height:	4 ¾", 12.1 cm
Colour:	Light brown shirt with dark patches, black hair, blue tie, light brown base
Issued:	1996 in a limited edition of 2,000

Beswick Number	Price			
	U.S. $	Can. $	U.K. £	Aust. $
3588	60.00	90.00	45.00	110.00

3590
DINO™

Designer:	Simon Ward
Height:	4 ¾", 12.1 cm
Colour:	Purple, white and black
Issued:	1997 in a limited edition of 2,000

Beswick Number	Price			
	U.S. $	Can. $	U.K. £	Aust. $
3590	80.00	125.00	55.00	150.00

TOP CAT
1996-1998

3581
TOP CAT™

Designer:	Andy Moss
Height:	4 ½", 11.9 cm
Colour:	Yellow cat wearing a mauve waistcoat and hat
Issued:	1996 in a limited edition of 2,000
Series:	Top Cat

John Beswick
TOP CAT ™
© 1996 H-B PROD . INC
LICENSED BY CPL
© 1996 ROYAL DOULTON
EXCLUSIVE EDITION OF 2,000
FOR THE DOULTON &
BESWICK FAIRS IN ENGLAND

Beswick Number	Price			
	U.S. $	*Can. $*	*U.K. £*	*Aust. $*
3581	65.00	95.00	40.00	100.00

3586
CHOO-CHOO™

Designer:	Andy Moss
Height:	4 ½", 11.9 cm
Colour:	Pink cat wearing a white shirt
Issued:	1996 in a limited edition of 2,000
Series:	Top Cat

John Beswick
CHOO-CHOO ™
© 1996 H-B PROD., INC.
LICENSED BY CPL
© 1996 ROYAL DOULTON
EXCLUSIVE EDITION OF 2,000
FOR THE DOULTON &
BESWICK FAIRS IN ENGLAND

Beswick Number	Price			
	U.S. $	*Can. $*	*U.K. £*	*Aust. $*
3586	65.00	95.00	40.00	100.00

3624
FANCY FANCY™

Designer:	Andy Moss
Height:	4 ½", 11.9 cm
Colour:	Pink cat with black tip on tail, white scarf
Issued:	1997 in a limited edition of 2,000
Series:	Top Cat

John Beswick
FANCY FANCY ™
© 1997 H-B PROD., INC.
LICENSED BY CPL
© 1997 ROYAL DOULTON
EXCLUSIVE EDITION OF 2,000
FOR THE DOULTON &
BESWICK FAIRS IN ENGLAND

Beswick Number	Price			
	U.S. $	Can. $	U.K. £	Aust. $
3624	60.00	80.00	35.00	90.00

3627
BENNY™

Designer:	Andy Moss
Height:	3 ¾", 8.5 cm
Colour:	Lilac cat wearing a white jacket
Issued:	1997 in a limited edition of 2,000
Series:	Top Cat

John Beswick
BENNY ™
© 1997 H-B PROD., INC.
LICENSED BY CPL
© 1997 ROYAL DOULTON
EXCLUSIVE EDITION OF 2,000
FOR THE DOULTON &
BESWICK FAIRS IN ENGLAND

Beswick Number	Price			
	U.S. $	Can. $	U.K. £	Aust. $
3627	60.00	80.00	35.00	90.00

3671
OFFICER DIBBLE™

Designer:	Andy Moss
Height:	6 ¾", 17.5 cm
Colour:	Dark blue police uniform
Issued:	1998 in a limited edition of 2,000
Series:	Top Cat

Beswick Number	Price			
	U.S. $	Can. $	U.K. £	Aust. $
3671	115.00	150.00	70.00	165.00

3673
SPOOK™

Designer:	Andy Moss
Height:	4 ½", 11.9 cm
Colour:	Beige cat with black tie
Issued:	1998 in a limited edition of 2,000
Series:	Top Cat

| Beswick | Price | | | |
Number	U.S. $	Can. $	U.K. £	Aust. $
3673	80.00	110.00	50.00	125.00

3674
BRAIN™

Designer:	Andy Moss
Height:	4", 10.1 cm
Colour:	Yellow cat wearing a purple shirt
Issued:	1998 in a limited edition of 2,000
Series:	Top Cat

| Beswick | Price | | | |
Number	U.S. $	Can. $	U.K. £	Aust. $
3674	80.00	110.00	50.00	125.00

HIPPOS ON HOLIDAY

HH1
GRANDMA™

Modeller:	Amanda Hughes-Lubeck
Height:	5", 12.7 cm
Colour:	Orange, grey, black and brown
Issued:	1999 in a limited edition of 3,500

Beswick Number		Price			
		U.S. $	Can. $	U.K. £	Aust. $
HH1	Complete Set	400.00	575.00	270.00	575.00

HH2
GRANDPA™

Modeller:	Warren Platt
Height:	5", 12.7 cm
Colour:	White jacket and cap, blue trousers
Issued:	1999 in a limited edition of 3,500

Beswick Number		Price			
		U.S. $	Can. $	U.K. £	Aust. $
HH2	Complete Set	400.00	575.00	270.00	575.00

HH3
MA™

Modeller:	Amanda Hughes-Lubeck
Height:	5", 12.7 cm
Colour:	Purple, grey, pink and yellow
Issued:	1999 in a limited edition of 3,500

Beswick Number		Price			
		U.S. $	Can. $	U.K. £	Aust. $
HH3	Complete Set	400.00	575.00	270.00	575.00

HH4
PA™

Modeller:	Martyn Alcock
Height:	5", 12.7 cm
Colour:	Yellow, green and grey
Issued:	1999 in a limited edition of 3,500

Beswick Number		Price			
		U.S. $	Can. $	U.K. £	Aust. $
HH4	Complete Set	400.00	575.00	270.00	575.00

HH5
HARRIET™

Modeller:	Martyn Alcock
Height:	5", 12.7 cm
Colour:	Pink and grey
Issued:	1999 in a limited edition of 3,500

Beswick Number		Price			
		U.S. $	Can. $	U.K. £	Aust. $
HH5	Complete Set	400.00	575.00	270.00	575.00

HH6
HUGO™

Modeller:	Warren Platt
Height:	4", 10.1 cm
Colour:	Grey , white, blue and yellow
Issued:	1999 in a limited edition of 3,500

Beswick Number		Price			
		U.S. $	Can. $	U.K. £	Aust. $
HH6	Complete Set	400.00	575.00	270.00	575.00

JANE HISSEY'S
OLD BEAR™
AND FRIENDS

OB4601
OLD BEAR™

Designer:	Jane Hissey
Modeller:	Paul Gurney
Height:	4", 10.1 cm
Colour:	Light brown bear
Issued:	1997 to the present

| Beswick | Price | | | |
Number	U.S. $	Can. $	U.K. £	Aust. $
OB4601	—	—	10.00	—

OB4602
TIME FOR BED™

Designer:	Jane Hissey
Modeller:	Paul Gurney
Height:	4", 10.1 cm
Colour:	Golden brown giraffe, light brown bear wearing blue and white striped pyjamas, yellow toothbrush
Issued:	1997 - 1999

| Beswick | Price | | | |
Number	U.S. $	Can. $	U.K. £	Aust. $
OB4602	25.00	35.00	15.00	35.00

OB4603
BRAMWELL BROWN HAS A GOOD IDEA™

Designer:	Jane Hissey
Modeller:	Paul Gurney
Height:	4", 10.1 cm
Colour:	Brown bear, beige teddy bear wearing red trousers, green and white base
Issued:	1997 - 1998

| Beswick | Price | | | |
Number	U.S. $	Can. $	U.K. £	Aust. $
OB4603	25.00	35.00	15.00	35.00

OB4604
DON'T WORRY RABBIT™

Designer:	Jane Hissey
Modeller:	Paul Gurney
Height:	4", 10.1 cm
Colour:	Light brown bear, beige rabbit, yellow and red block, green base
Issued:	1997 - 2000

Beswick Number	Price			
	U.S. $	Can. $	U.K. £	Aust. $
OB4604	20.00	35.00	15.00	35.00

OB4605
THE LONG RED SCARF™

Designer:	Jane Hissey
Modeller:	Paul Gurney
Height:	4", 10.1 cm
Colour:	Golden brown giraffe wearing long red scarf, dark brown bear
Issued:	1997 - 1999

Beswick Number	Price			
	U.S. $	Can. $	U.K. £	Aust. $
OB4605	30.00	50.00	20.00	50.00

OB4606
WAITING FOR SNOW™

Designer:	Jane Hissey
Modeller:	Paul Gurney
Height:	4", 10.1 cm
Colour:	Golden brown giraffe, light brown bear, white duck with brown beak
Issued:	1997 - 1999

Beswick Number	Price			
	U.S. $	Can. $	U.K. £	Aust. $
OB4606	25.00	45.00	17.00	45.00

OB4607
THE SNOWFLAKE BISCUITS™

Designer: Jane Hissey
Modeller: Paul Gurney
Height: 4", 10.1 cm
Colour: Golden brown giraffe wearing red scarf, light brown bear wearing red dungarees, white donkey with black stripes, brown biscuits
Issued: 1997 to the present

| Beswick | Price | | | |
Number	U.S. $	Can. $	U.K. £	Aust. $
OB4607	—	—	20.00	—

OB4608
WELCOME HOME, OLD BEAR™

Designer: Jane Hissey
Modeller: Paul Gurney
Height: 4", 10.1 cm
Colour: Brown bear with two light brown bears and a white duck
Issued: 1997 to the present

| Beswick | Price | | | |
Number	U.S. $	Can. $	U.K. £	Aust. $
OB4608	—	—	15.00	—

OB4609
RUFF'S PRIZE™

Designer: Jane Hissey
Modeller: Paul Gurney
Height: 2 ½", 6.5 cm
Colour: Light brown dog wearing a dark brown coat, light brown bear wearing red dungarees
Issued: 1997 - 1999

| Beswick | Price | | | |
Number	U.S. $	Can. $	U.K. £	Aust. $
OB4609	20.00	35.00	15.00	35.00

OB4610
TIME FOR A CUDDLE, HUG ME TIGHT™

Designer:	Jane Hissey
Modeller:	Paul Gurney
Height:	3 ½", 8.9 cm
Colour:	Golden brown bear, light brown bear wearing blue and white striped pyjamas
Issued:	1997 - 2000

Beswick Number	Price			
	U.S. $	Can. $	U.K. £	Aust. $
OB4610	20.00	35.00	15.00	35.00

OB4611
DON'T FORGET OLD BEAR™

Designer:	Jane Hissey
Modeller:	Paul Gurney
Height:	3", 7.6 cm
Colour:	Brown bear in brown box, red book covers
Issued:	1998 to the present

Beswick Number	Price			
	U.S. $	Can. $	U.K. £	Aust. $
OB4611	—	—	15.00	—

OB4612
HOLD ON TIGHT™

Designer:	Jane Hissey
Modeller:	Paul Gurney
Height:	3", 7.6 cm
Colour:	White owl wearing blue apron, light brown bear wearing blue and white striped pyjamas
Issued:	1998 to the present

Beswick Number	Price			
	U.S. $	Can. $	U.K. £	Aust. $
OB4612	—	—	12.00	—

OB4613
RESTING WITH CAT™

Designer:	Jane Hissey
Modeller:	Paul Gurney
Height:	2 ½", 6.4 cm
Colour:	Black cat with red inner ears and necktie, light brown bear wearing red trousers
Issued:	1998 to the present

Beswick Number		Price		
	U.S. $	Can. $	U.K. £	Aust. $
OB4613	—	—	15.00	—

OB4614
LOOKING FOR A SAILOR™

Designer:	Jane Hissey
Modeller:	Paul Gurney
Height:	5", 12.7 cm
Colour:	Red and blue horse, light brown bear
Issued:	1998 to the present

Beswick Number		Price		
	U.S. $	Can. $	U.K. £	Aust. $
OB4614	—	—	15.00	—

OB4615
TOO MUCH FOOD™

Designer:	Jane Hissey
Modeller:	Paul Gurney
Height:	4", 10.1 cm
Colour:	Golden brown bear on a brown basket, light brown bear wearing red trousers
Issued:	1998 to the present

Beswick Number		Price		
	U.S. $	Can. $	U.K. £	Aust. $
OB4615	—	—	15.00	—

OB4616
NEST OF SOCKS™

Designer:	Jane Hissey
Modeller:	Paul Gurney
Height:	2 ¾", 7.0 cm
Colour:	Pale brown, blue, green, white yellow and red
Issued:	2000 to the present

Beswick Number	U.S. $	Can. $	Price U.K. £	Aust. $
OB4616	—	—	16.00	—

OB4617
SNOW DECORATIONS™

Designer:	Jane Hissey
Modeller:	Paul Gurney
Height:	3 ½", 8.9 cm
Colour:	Brown bear
Issued:	2000 to the present

Beswick Number	U.S. $	Can. $	Price U.K. £	Aust. $
OB4617	—	—	12.00	—

OB4618
STORYTIME™

Designer:	Jane Hissey
Modeller:	Paul Gurney
Height:	2 ½", 6.4 cm
Colour:	Black, beige, red, light blue, and white
Issued:	2000 to the present

Beswick Number	U.S. $	Can. $	Price U.K. £	Aust. $
OB4618	—	—	14.00	—

OB4619
DUCK™

Designer:	Jane Hissey
Modeller:	Paul Gurney
Height:	3", 7.6 cm
Colour:	White, brown and yellow duck, multicoloured quilt
Issued:	2000 to the present

Beswick	Price			
Number	U.S. $	Can. $	U.K. £	Aust. $
OB4619	—	—	12.00	—

OB4620
UP, UP AND AWAY™

Designer:	Jane Hissey
Modeller:	Paul Gurney
Height:	3 ½", 8.9 cm
Colour:	White, red, brown, blue and silver
Issued:	2000 to the present

Beswick	Price			
Number	U.S. $	Can. $	U.K. £	Aust. $
OB4620	—	—	14.00	—

JOAN WALSH ANGLUND

2272
ANGLUND BOY™

Designer:	Albert Hallam
Height:	4 ½", 11.9 cm
Colour:	Green dungarees, brown hat
Issued:	1970 - 1971

Beswick Number		Price		
	U.S. $	Can. $	U.K. £	Aust. $
2272	175.00	250.00	115.00	250.00

2293
ANGLUND GIRL WITH DOLL™

Designer:	Albert Hallam
Height:	4 ½", 11.9 cm
Colour:	Green dress and bow, white apron
Issued:	1970 - 1971

Beswick Number		Price		
	U.S. $	Can. $	U.K. £	Aust. $
2293	175.00	250.00	115.00	250.00

2317
ANGLUND GIRL WITH FLOWERS™

Designer:	Albert Hallam
Height:	4 ¾", 12.1 cm
Colour:	White dress, blue leggings, straw hat with blue ribbon
Issued:	1971 - 1971

Beswick Number		Price		
	U.S. $	Can. $	U.K. £	Aust. $
2317	175.00	250.00	115.00	250.00

KITTY MACBRIDE

2526
A FAMILY MOUSE™

Designer:	Graham Tongue
Height:	3 ½", 8.9 cm
Colour:	Brown, mauve and turquoise, light and dark green base
Issued:	1975 - 1983

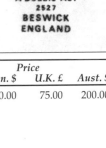

Beswick Number	Price			
	U.S. $	Can. $	U.K. £	Aust. $
2526	135.00	200.00	75.00	200.00

2527
A DOUBLE ACT™

Designer:	Graham Tongue
Height:	3 ½", 8.9 cm
Colour:	Yellow, orange, brown, green and blue
Issued:	1975 - 1983

Beswick Number	Price			
	U.S. $	Can. $	U.K. £	Aust. $
2527	135.00	200.00	75.00	200.00

2528
THE RACEGOER™

Designer:	David Lyttleton
Height:	3 ½", 8.9 cm
Colour:	Brown and yellow, light and dark green base
Issued:	1975 - 1983

Beswick Number	Price			
	U.S. $	Can. $	U.K. £	Aust. $
2528	115.00	175.00	75.00	175.00

2529
A GOOD READ™

Designer:	David Lyttleton
Height:	2 ½", 6.4 cm
Colour:	Yellow, blue, brown and white
Issued:	1975 - 1983

Beswick Number	Price			
	U.S. $	Can. $	U.K. £	Aust. $
2529	325.00	475.00	175.00	475.00

2530
LAZYBONES™

Designer:	David Lyttleton
Height:	1 ½", 3.8 cm
Colour:	Blue, black and brown, green and white base
Issued:	1975 - 1983

Beswick Number	Price			
	U.S. $	Can. $	U.K. £	Aust. $
2530	135.00	200.00	75.00	200.00

2531
A SNACK™

Designer:	David Lyttleton
Height:	3 ¼", 8.3 cm
Colour:	Brown, blue and yellow, green base
Issued:	1975 - 1983

Beswick Number	Price			
	U.S. $	Can. $	U.K. £	Aust. $
2531	100.00	150.00	70.00	150.00

2532
STRAINED RELATIONS™

Designer:	David Lyttleton
Height:	3", 7.6 cm
Colour:	Brown, blue and green
Issued:	1975 - 1983

Beswick Number	Price			
	U.S. $	Can. $	U.K. £	Aust. $
2532	115.00	175.00	75.00	175.00

2533
JUST GOOD FRIENDS™

Designer:	David Lyttleton
Height:	3", 7.6 cm
Colour:	Brown, yellow, blue, red and green
Issued:	1975 - 1983

Beswick Number	Price			
	U.S. $	Can. $	U.K. £	Aust. $
2533	160.00	265.00	100.00	250.00

2565
THE RING™

Designer:	David Lyttleton
Height:	3 ¼", 8.3 cm
Colour:	Brown, white, purple and yellow
Issued:	1976 - 1983

Beswick Number	Price			
	U.S. $	Can. $	U.K. £	Aust. $
2565	200.00	300.00	125.00	275.00

2566
GUILTY SWEETHEARTS™

Designer:	David Lyttleton
Height:	2 ¼", 5.7 cm
Colour:	Brown, yellow, green and white
Issued:	1976 - 1983

Beswick Number	Price			
	U.S. $	Can. $	U.K. £	Aust. $
2566	175.00	250.00	115.00	225.00

2589
ALL I DO IS THINK OF YOU™

Designer:	David Lyttleton
Height:	2 ½", 6.4 cm
Colour:	Brown, yellow and white
Issued:	1976 - 1983

Beswick Number	Price			
	U.S. $	Can. $	U.K. £	Aust. $
2589	500.00	600.00	325.00	625.00

LITTLE LIKEABLES

LL1
FAMILY GATHERING™
(Hen and Two Chicks)

Designer:	Diane Griffiths
Height:	4 ½", 11.9 cm
Colour:	White hen and chicks with yellow beaks and gold comb on hen
Issued:	1985 - 1987

Beswick Number	Price			
	U.S. $	Can. $	U.K. £	Aust. $
LL1	80.00	125.00	50.00	125.00

LL2
WATCHING THE WORLD GO BY™
(Frog)

Designer:	Robert Tabbenor
Height:	3 ¾", 9.5 cm
Colour:	White frog, black and green eyes
Issued:	1985 - 1987

Beswick Number	Price			
	U.S. $	Can. $	U.K. £	Aust. $
LL2	80.00	125.00	50.00	125.00

LL3
HIDE AND SLEEP™
(Pig and Two Piglets)

Designer:	Robert Tabbenor
Height:	3 ¼", 8.3 cm
Colour:	White pigs with pink noses, ears and tails
Issued:	1985 - 1987

Beswick Number	Price			
	U.S. $	Can. $	U.K. £	Aust. $
LL3	80.00	125.00	50.00	125.00

LL4
MY PONY™
(Pony)

Designer:	Diane Griffiths
Height:	7 ¼", 18.4 cm
Colour:	White pony with blue highlights in mane and tail
Issued:	1985 - 1987

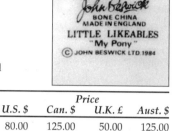

Beswick Number	Price			
	U.S. $	*Can. $*	*U.K. £*	*Aust. $*
LL4	80.00	125.00	50.00	125.00

LL5
ON TOP OF THE WORLD™
(Elephant)

Designer:	Diane Griffiths
Height:	3 ¾", 9.5 cm
Colour:	White elephant with black eyes and gold nails
Issued:	1985 - 1987

Beswick Number	Price			
	U.S. $	*Can. $*	*U.K. £*	*Aust. $*
LL5	80.00	125.00	50.00	125.00

LL6
TREAT ME GENTLY™
(Fawn)

Designer:	Diane Griffiths
Height:	4 ½", 11.9 cm
Colour:	White fawn with black and brown eyes, black nose and gold hoof
Issued:	1985 - 1987

Beswick Number	Price			
	U.S. $	*Can. $*	*U.K. £*	*Aust. $*
LL6	80.00	125.00	50.00	125.00

LL7
OUT AT LAST™
(Duckling)

Designer:	Robert Tabbenor
Height:	3 ¼", 8.3 cm
Colour:	White duck with black and brown eyes and gold beak
Issued:	1985 - 1987

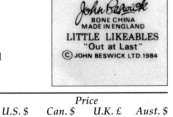

Beswick Number	Price			
	U.S. $	Can. $	U.K. £	Aust. $
LL7	80.00	125.00	50.00	125.00

LL8
CATS CHORUS™
(Cats)

Designer:	Robert Tabbenor
Height:	4 ¾", 12.1 cm
Colour:	Two white cats with black and green eyes, black nose, pink ears and mouth
Issued:	1985 - 1987

Beswick Number	Price			
	U.S. $	Can. $	U.K. £	Aust. $
LL8	80.00	125.00	50.00	125.00

LITTLE LOVABLES

LL1
HAPPY BIRTHDAY™

Designer:	Amanda Hughes-Lubeck
Height:	4 ½", 11.9 cm
Colour:	White, pink and orange (gloss)
Issued:	1992 - 1994
Varieties:	LL8; LL15; also unnamed LL22

LL 1

Model No.	Price			
	U.S. $	Can. $	U.K. £	Aust. $
3328	35.00	45.00	20.00	50.00

LL2
I LOVE YOU™

Designer:	Amanda Hughes-Lubeck
Height:	4 ½", 11.9 cm
Colour:	White, green and pink (gloss)
Issued:	1992 - 1994
Varieties:	LL9, LL16; also unnamed LL23

LL 2

Model No.	Price			
	U.S. $	Can. $	U.K. £	Aust. $
3320	35.00	45.00	20.00	50.00

LL3
GOD LOVES ME™

Designer:	Amanda Hughes-Lubeck
Height:	3 ¾", 9.5 cm
Colour:	White, green and turquoise (gloss)
Issued:	1992 - 1993
Varieties:	LL10, LL17; also called Please, LL33, LL34; also unnamed LL24

LL 3

Model No.	Price			
	U.S. $	Can. $	U.K. £	Aust. $
3336	125.00	200.00	90.00	200.00

LL4
JUST FOR YOU™

Designer:	Warren Platt
Height:	4 ½", 11.9 cm
Colour:	White, pink and blue (gloss)
Issued:	1992 - 1994
Varieties:	LL11, LL18; also unnamed LL25

Model No.	Price			
	U.S. $	Can. $	U.K. £	Aust. $
3361	35.00	45.00	20.00	50.00

LL5
TO MOTHER™

Designer:	Amanda Hughes-Lubeck
Height:	4 ½", 11.9 cm
Colour:	White, blue and purple (gloss)
Issued:	1992 - 1994
Varieties:	LL12, LL19; also called To Daddy, also unnamed LL26

Model No.	Price			
	U.S. $	Can. $	U.K. £	Aust. $
3331	35.00	45.00	20.00	50.00

LL6
CONGRATULATIONS™

Designer:	Warren Platt
Height:	4 ½", 11.9 cm
Colour:	White, green and pink (gloss)
Issued:	1992 - 1994
Varieties:	LL13, LL20; also unnamed LL27

Model No.	Price			
	U.S. $	Can. $	U.K. £	Aust. $
3340	35.00	45.00	20.00	50.00

LL7
PASSED™

Designer:	Amanda Hughes-Lubeck
Height:	3", 7.6 cm
Colour:	White, lilac and pink (gloss)
Issued:	1992 - 1994
Varieties:	LL14, LL21; also unnamed LL28

Model No.	Price			
	U.S. $	Can. $	U.K. £	Aust. $
3334	45.00	70.00	30.00	70.00

LL8
HAPPY BIRTHDAY™

Designer:	Amanda Hughes-Lubeck
Height:	4 ½", 11.9 cm
Colour:	White, yellow and green (gloss)
Issued:	1992 - 1994
Varieties:	LL1, LL15; also unnamed LL22

Model No.	Price			
	U.S. $	Can. $	U.K. £	Aust. $
3328	35.00	45.00	20.00	50.00

LL9
I LOVE YOU™

Designer:	Amanda Hughes-Lubeck
Height:	4 ½", 11.9 cm
Colour:	White, blue and orange (gloss)
Issued:	1992 - 1994
Varieties:	LL2, LL16; also unnamed LL23

Model No.	Price			
	U.S. $	Can. $	U.K. £	Aust. $
3320	35.00	45.00	20.00	50.00

LL10
GOD LOVES ME™

Designer:	Amanda Hughes-Lubeck
Height:	3 ¾", 9.5 cm
Colour:	White, gold and blue (gloss)
Issued:	1992 - 1993
Varieties:	LL3, LL17; also called Please, LL33, LL34; also unnamed LL24

Model No.	Price			
	U.S. $	Can. $	U.K. £	Aust. $
3336	110.00	175.00	70.00	175.00

LL11
JUST FOR YOU™

Designer:	Warren Platt
Height:	4 ½", 11.9 cm
Colour:	White, yellow and pale green (gloss)
Issued:	1992 - 1994
Varieties:	LL4, LL18; also unnamed LL25

Model No.	Price			
	U.S. $	Can. $	U.K. £	Aust. $
3361	35.00	45.00	20.00	50.00

LL12
TO MOTHER™

Designer:	Amanda Hughes-Lubeck
Height:	4 ½", 11.9 cm
Colour:	White, yellow and pink (gloss)
Issued:	1992 - 1994
Varieties:	LL5, LL19; also called To Daddy, LL29; also unnamed LL26

Model No.	Price			
	U.S. $	Can. $	U.K. £	Aust. $
3331	35.00	45.00	20.00	50.00

LL13
CONGRATULATIONS™

Designer:	Warren Platt
Height:	4 ½", 11.9 cm
Colour:	White, pale blue and yellow (gloss)
Issued:	1992 - 1994
Varieties:	LL6, LL20; also unnamed LL27

Model	Price			
No.	U.S. $	Can. $	U.K. £	Aust. $
3340	35.00	45.00	25.00	50.00

LL14
PASSED™

Designer:	Amanda Hughes-Lubeck
Height:	3", 7.6 cm
Colour:	White, light blue and orange (gloss)
Issued:	1992 - 1994
Varieties:	LL7, LL21; also unnamed LL28

Model	Price			
No.	U.S. $	Can. $	U.K. £	Aust. $
3334	45.00	65.00	30.00	65.00

LL15
HAPPY BIRTHDAY™

Designer:	Amanda Hughes-Lubeck
Height:	4 ½", 11.9cm
Colour:	White, salmon and green (matt)
Issued:	1992 - 1993
Varieties:	LL8, LL15; also unnamed LL22

Model	Price			
No.	U.S. $	Can. $	U.K. £	Aust. $
3407	125.00	175.00	75.00	175.00

LL16
I LOVE YOU™

Designer:	Amanda Hughes-Lubeck
Height:	4 ½", 11.9 cm
Colour:	White, green and yellow (matt)
Issued:	1992 - 1993
Varieties:	LL2, LL9; also unnamed LL23

Model No.	Price			
	U.S. $	*Can. $*	*U.K. £*	*Aust. $*
3406	125.00	175.00	85.00	175.00

LL17
GOD LOVES ME™

Designer:	Amanda Hughes-Lubeck
Height:	3 ¾", 9.5 cm
Colour:	White, purple and yellow (matt)
Issued:	1992 - 1993
Varieties:	LL3, LL10; also called Please, LL33, LL34; also unnamed LL24

Model No.	Price			
	U.S. $	*Can. $*	*U.K. £*	*Aust. $*
3410	125.00	175.00	85.00	175.00

LL18
JUST FOR YOU™

Designer:	Warren Platt
Height:	4 ½", 11.9 cm
Colour:	White, yellow and dark blue (matt)
Issued:	1992 - 1993
Varieties:	LL4, LL11; also unnamed LL25

Model No.	Price			
	U.S. $	*Can. $*	*U.K. £*	*Aust. $*
3412	125.00	175.00	75.00	175.00

LL19
TO MOTHER™

Designer:	Amanda Hughes-Lubeck
Height:	4 ½", 11.9 cm
Colour:	White, green and orange (matt)
Issued:	1992 - 1993
Varieties:	LL5, LL12; also called To Daddy, LL29; also unnamed LL26

Model	Price			
No.	U.S. $	Can. $	U.K. £	Aust. $
3408	125.00	175.00	85.00	175.00

LL20
CONGRATULATIONS™

Designer:	Warren Platt
Height:	4 ½", 11.9 cm
Colour:	White, blue and red (matt)
Issued:	1992 - 1993
Varieties:	LL6, LL13; also unnamed LL27

Model	Price			
No.	U.S. $	Can. $	U.K. £	Aust. $
3411	125.00	175.00	85.00	175.00

LL21
PASSED™

Designer:	Amanda Hughes-Lubeck
Height:	3", 7.6 cm
Colour:	White, blue and orange (matt)
Issued:	1992 - 1993
Varieties:	LL7, LL14; also unnamed LL28

Model	Price			
No.	U.S. $	Can. $	U.K. £	Aust. $
3409	125.00	175.00	85.00	175.00

LL22
(No Name)

Designer:	Unknown
Height:	4 ½", 11.9 cm
Colour:	White, pink and orange (gloss)
Issued:	1993 - 1993
Varieties:	Also called Happy Birthday, LL1, LL8, LL15

Model No.	Price			
	U.S. $	Can. $	U.K. £	Aust. $
3329	90.00	125.00	60.00	125.00

LL23
(No Name)

Designer:	Amanda Hughes-Lubeck
Height:	4 ½", 11.9 cm
Colour:	White, green and pink (gloss)
Issued:	1993 - 1993
Varieties:	Also called I Love You, LL2, LL9, LL16

Model No.	Price			
	U.S. $	Can. $	U.K. £	Aust. $
3320	90.00	125.00	60.00	125.00

LL24
(No Name)

Designer:	Amanda Hughes-Lubeck
Height:	3 ¾", 9.5 cm
Colour:	White, green and turquoise (gloss)
Issued:	1993 - 1993
Varieties:	Also called God Loves Me, LL3. LL10, LL17; Please, LL33, LL34

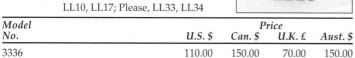

Model No.	Price			
	U.S. $	Can. $	U.K. £	Aust. $
3336	110.00	150.00	70.00	150.00

LL25
(No Name)

Designer:	Warren Platt
Height:	4 ½", 11.9 cm
Colour:	White, pink and blue (gloss)
Issued:	1993 - 1993
Varieties:	Also called Just For You, LL4, LL11, LL18

Model No.	Price			
	U.S. $	Can. $	U.K. £	Aust. $
3361	90.00	125.00	60.00	125.00

LL26
(No Name)

Designer:	Amanda Hughes-Lubeck
Height:	4 ¼", 10.8 cm
Colour:	White, blue and purple (gloss)
Issued:	1993 - 1993
Varieties:	Also called To Mother, LL5, LL12, LL19;To Daddy, LL29

Model No.	Price			
	U.S. $	Can. $	U.K. £	Aust. $
3331	90.00	125.00	60.00	125.00

LL27
(No Name)

Designer:	Warren Platt
Height:	4 ½", 11.9 cm
Colour:	White, green and pink (gloss)
Issued:	1993 - 1993
Varieties:	Also called Congratulations, LL6, LL13, LL20

Model No.	Price			
	U.S. $	Can. $	U.K. £	Aust. $
3340	90.00	125.00	60.00	125.00

LL28
(No Name)

Designer: Amanda Hughes-Lubeck
Height: 3", 7.6 cm
Colour: White, lilac and pink (gloss)
Issued: 1993 - 1993
Varieties: Also called Passed, LL7,
LL14, LL21

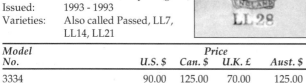

| Model | Price | | | |
No.	U.S. $	Can. $	U.K. £	Aust. $
3334	90.00	125.00	70.00	125.00

LL29
TO DADDY™

Designer: Amanda Hughes-Lubeck
Height: 4 ½", 11.9 cm
Colour: White, light blue and
green (gloss)
Issued: 1994 - 1994
Varieties: Also called To Mother, LL5,
LL12, LL19; also unnamed LL26

| Model | Price | | | |
No.	U.S. $	Can. $	U.K. £	Aust. $
3331	55.00	75.00	35.00	75.00

LL30
MERRY CHRISTMAS™

Designer: Amanda Hughes-Lubeck
Height: 4", 10.1 cm
Colour: White, red and green (gloss)
Issued: 1993 - 1994

| Model | Price | | | |
No.	U.S. $	Can. $	U.K. £	Aust. $
3389	80.00	110.00	45.00	110.00

LL31
GOOD LUCK™

Designer:	Amanda Hughes-Lubeck
Height:	4 ¼", 10.8 cm
Colour:	White, pink and green (gloss)
Issued:	1993 - 1994

Model	Price			
No.	U.S. $	Can. $	U.K. £	Aust. $
3388	80.00	125.00	45.00	125.00

LL32
GET WELL SOON™

Designer:	Amanda Hughes-Lubeck
Height:	4 ¼", 10.8 cm
Colour:	White, green and purple (gloss)
Issued:	1994 - 1994

Model	Price			
No.	U.S. $	Can. $	U.K. £	Aust. $
3390	80.00	125.00	45.00	125.00

LL33
PLEASE™

Designer:	Amanda Hughes-Lubeck
Height:	3 ¾", 9.5 cm
Colour:	White, green and blue (gloss)
Issued:	1993 - 1994
Varieties:	LL34; also called God Loves Me, LL3, LL10, LL17; also unnamed LL24

Model	Price			
No.	U.S. $	Can. $	U.K. £	Aust. $
3336	50.00	65.00	30.00	65.00

LL34
PLEASE™

Designer: Amanda Hughes-Lubeck
Height: 3 ¾", 9.5 cm
Colour: White, gold and light blue (gloss)
Issued: 1993 - 1994
Varieties: LL33; also called God Loves Me,
LL3, LL10, LL17; also unnamed LL24

| Model | Price | | | |
No.	U.S. $	Can. $	U.K. £	Aust. $
3336	50.00	65.00	30.00	65.00

LL35 is the prototype for "I Love Beswick." Colourway not issued.

LL36
I LOVE BESWICK™

Designer: Amanda Hughes-Lubeck
Height: 4 ½", 11.9 cm
Colour: White, green and pink (gloss)
Issued: 1995 - 1995
Varieties: Also called I Love You, LL2, LL9,
LL16; also unnamed LL23

| Model | Price | | | |
No.	U.S. $	Can. $	U.K. £	Aust. $
3320	225.00	300.00	125.00	275.00

Note: This piece was specially commissioned for the 10th Anniversary of the Beswick Collectors Circle.

NORMAN THELWELL

EARTHENWARE SERIES
RESIN STUDIO SCULPTURES

NORMAN THELWELL

EARTHENWARE SERIES 1981-1989

2704A
AN ANGEL ON HORSEBACK™
First Variation

Designer:	Harry Sales
Modeller:	David Lyttleton
Height:	4 ½", 11.4 cm
Colour:	Grey horse, rider wears brown jumper, yellow jodhpurs
Issued:	1981 - 1989
Varieties:	2704B

Beswick	Price			
Number	U.S. $	Can. $	U.K. £	Aust. $
2704A	250.00	425.00	150.00	400.00

2704B
AN ANGEL ON HORSEBACK™
Second Variation

Designer:	Harry Sales
Modeller:	David Lyttleton
Height:	4 ½", 11.4 cm
Colour:	Bay horse, rider wears red jumper, yellow jodhpurs
Issued:	1981 - 1989
Varieties:	2704A

Beswick	Price			
Number	U.S. $	Can. $	U.K. £	Aust. $
2704B	225.00	400.00	125.00	400.00

2769A
KICK-START™
First Variation

Designer:	Harry Sales
Modeller:	David Lyttleton
Height:	3 ½", 8.9 cm
Colour:	Grey horse, rider wears red jersey and yellow pants
Issued:	1982 - 1989
Varieties:	2769B

Beswick	Price			
Number	U.S. $	Can. $	U.K. £	Aust. $
2769A	250.00	425.00	150.00	425.00

2769B
KICK-START™
Second Variation

Designer:	Harry Sales
Modeller:	David Lyttleton
Height:	3 ½", 8.9 cm
Colour:	Bay horse, rider wears red jersey and yellow pants
Issued:	1982 - 1989
Varieties:	2769B

Beswick Number	Price			
	U.S. $	Can. $	U.K. £	Aust. $
2769B	225.00	400.00	125.00	375.00

2789A
PONY EXPRESS™
First Variation

Designer:	Harry Sales
Modeller:	David Lyttleton
Height:	4 ½", 11.4 cm
Colour:	Grey horse, rider wears green jersey and yellow trousers
Issued:	1982 - 1989
Varieties:	2789B

Beswick Number	Price			
	U.S. $	Can. $	U.K. £	Aust. $
2789A	250.00	425.00	150.00	425.00

2789B
PONY EXPRESS™
Second Variation

Designer:	Harry Sales
Modeller:	David Lyttleton
Height:	4 ½", 11.4 cm
Colour:	Bay horse, rider wears red jersey and yellow pants
Issued:	1982 - 1989
Varieties:	2789A

Beswick Number	Price			
	U.S. $	Can. $	U.K. £	Aust. $
2789B	225.00	400.00	125.00	425.00

NORMAN THEWELL

RESIN STUDIO SCULPTURES — 1985-1985

SS7A
I FORGIVE YOU™
First Variation

Designer:	Harry Sales
Modeller:	David Lyttleton
Height:	4", 10.1 cm
Colour:	Grey horse, rider wears red jacket and yellow pants
Issued:	1985 - 1985
Series:	Studio Sculptures
Varieties:	SS7B

Beswick	Price			
Number	U.S. $	Can. $	U.K. £	Aust. $
SS7A	225.00	375.00	125.00	350.00

SS7B
I FORGIVE YOU™
Second Variation

Designer:	Harry Sales
Modeller:	David Lyttleton
Height:	4", 10.1 cm
Colour:	Bay horse, rider wears red jacket and yellow pants
Issued:	1985 - 1985
Series:	Studio Sculptures
Varieties:	SS7A

Beswick	Price			
Number	U.S. $	Can. $	U.K. £	Aust. $
SS7B	225.00	375.00	125.00	350.00

SS12A
EARLY BATH™
First Variation

Designer:	Harry Sales
Modeller:	David Lyttleton
Height:	4 ¾", 12.1 cm
Colour:	Grey horse, rider wears red jacket and yellow pants
Issued:	1985 - 1985
Series:	Studio Sculptures
Varieties:	SS12B

Beswick	Price			
Number	U.S. $	Can. $	U.K. £	Aust. $
SS12A	225.00	375.00	150.00	375.00

SS12B
EARLY BATH™
Second Variation

Designer:	Harry Sales
Height:	4 ¾", 12.1 cm
Colour:	Bay horse, rider wears red jacket and yellow pants
Issued:	1985 - 1985
Series:	Studio Sculptures
Varieties:	SS12A

Beswick Number	Price			
	U.S. $	Can. $	U.K. £	Aust. $
SS12B	225.00	375.00	150.00	375.00

JOAN WALSH ANGLUND™

Anglund Girl with Doll

Anglund Girl with Flowers

Anglund Boy

KITTY MACBRIDE™

A Family Mouse

Just Good Friends

The Ring

LITTLE LOVABLES™

Just For You

God Loves Me

Congratulations

NORMAN THELWELL™
EARTHENWARE SERIES

Pony Express, First Variation

Pony Express, Second Variation

An Angel on Horseback, First Variation

An Angel on Horseback, Second Variation

Kick-Start, First Variation

Kick-Start, Second Variation

PADDINGTON BEAR™

Paddington The Fisherman

Paddington The Golfer

ST. TIGGYWINKLES™

A Helping Hand

Friends

THE SNOWMAN GIFT COLLECTION™

Highland Snowman

Stylish Snowman

Thank You Snowman

Cellist Snowman

The Snowman Skiing

Cymbal Player Snowman

DISNEY PRINCESS COLLECTION™

Cinderella

Snow White, Style Two

Jasmine

Aurora

Ariel

Belle

DISNEY VILLAINS COLLECTION™

Cruella De Vil, Style Two

The Witch

Maleficent

101 DALMATIANS™

Lucky

Cruella De Vil, Style One

Pongo

Penny and Freckles

Penny

Patch, Rolly and Freckles

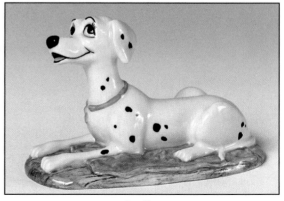

Perdita

SNOW WHITE AND THE SEVEN DWARFS™
SERIES TWO

Grumpy

Snow White

Dopey

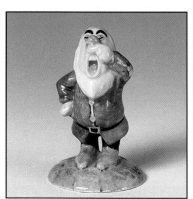

Happy

Bashful

Sneezy

Doc

Sleepy

MICKEY MOUSE COLLECTION™

Mickey Mouse, Style Two

Goofy, Style Two

Donald Duck, Style Two

WINNIE THE POOH™

Pooh Counting the Honeypots

Eeyore's Birthday

Pooh Lights the Candle

PETER PAN™

Smee

Peter Pan

Tinker Bell

NURSERY RHYMES
COLLECTION

DNR1
HUMPTY DUMPTY™

Designer:	Andy Moss
Height:	5 ½", 14.0 cm
Colour:	Red, pink, orange and black
Issued:	1998 in a special edition of 1,500
Series:	Nursery Rhymes Collection

Doulton Number	Price			
	U.S. $	Can. $	U.K. £	Aust. $
DNR1	100.00	150.00	68.00	175.00

DNR2
LITTLE MISS MUFFET™

Designer:	Andy Moss
Height:	6", 15.0 cm
Colour:	Pink dress and hair ribbon, white apron and collar, red shoes, black spider
Issued:	1998 in a special edition of 1,500
Series:	Nursery Rhymes Collection

Doulton Number	Price			
	U.S. $	Can. $	U.K. £	Aust. $
DNR2	125.00	175.00	78.00	200.00

DNR3
OLD MOTHER HUBBARD™

Designer:	Andy Moss
Height:	7 ½", 19.1 cm
Colour:	Red and green dress, blue and white apron and cap, black dog
Issued:	1999 in a special edition of 1,500
Series:	Nursery Rhymes Collection

Doulton Number	Price			
	U.S. $	Can. $	U.K. £	Aust. $
DNR3	125.00	175.00	78.00	200.00

DNR4
THE CAT AND THE FIDDLE™

Designer:	Andy Moss
Height:	6", 15.0 cm
Colour:	Black jacket and shoes, white waistcoat with red dots, grey trousers
Issued:	1999 in a special edition of 1,500
Series:	Nursery Rhymes Collection

Doulton Number	Price			
	U.S. $	Can. $	U.K. £	Aust. $
DNR4	125.00	175.00	78.00	200.00

DNR5
OLD KING COLE™

Designer:	Andy Moss
Height:	7", 17.8 cm
Colour:	Red, white, yellow and brown
Issued:	2000 in a special edition of 1,500
Series:	Nursery Rhymes Collection

Doulton Number	Price			
	U.S. $	Can. $	U.K. £	Aust. $
DNR5	125.00	175.00	78.00	200.00

PADDINGTON BEAR CO. LTD.

RESIN SERIES 1996-1998
CERAMIC SERIES 1999 to date

RESIN SERIES
1996 - 1998

PB1
PADDINGTON AT THE STATION™
Style One

Designer:	Zoe Annand
Modeller:	Zoe Annand
Height:	4 ¼", 10.8 cm
Colour:	Brown bear, blue coat, yellow hat, brown cobbled base
Issued:	1996 - 1998

Royal Doulton
Paddington™
"At the Station"
PB1
© Paddington & Co. Ltd. 1996
Licensed by ©OPYRIGHTS

Doulton Number		Price		
	U.S. $	Can. $	U.K. £	Aust. $
PB1	30.00	40.00	20.00	40.00

PB2
PADDINGTON BAKES A CAKE™

Designer:	Zoe Annand
Modeller:	Zoe Annand
Height:	4 ¼", 10.8 cm
Colour:	Red jacket, black hat, multicoloured cake, blue and white striped bowl
Issued:	1996 - 1998

Royal Doulton
Paddington™
"Bakes a Cake"
PB2
© Paddington & Co. Ltd. 1996
Licensed by ©OPYRIGHTS

Doulton Number		Price		
	U.S. $	Can. $	U.K. £	Aust. $
PB2	30.00	40.00	20.00	40.00

PB3
PADDINGTON DECORATING™

Designer:	Zoe Annand
Modeller:	Zoe Annand
Height:	4 ¾", 12.0 cm
Colour:	Blue coat, red hat, silver bucket, cream paint
Issued:	1996 - 1998

Royal Doulton
Paddington™
"Decorating"
PB3
© Paddington & Co. Ltd. 1996
Licensed by ©OPYRIGHTS

Doulton Number		Price		
	U.S. $	Can. $	U.K. £	Aust. $
PB3	30.00	40.00	20.00	40.00

PB4
PADDINGTON SURFING™

Designer:	Zoe Annand
Modeller:	Zoe Annand
Height:	4", 10.1 cm
Colour:	Multicoloured shorts, blue hat, yellow surfboard, red rubber ring, brown suitcase
Issued:	1996 - 1998

Royal Doulton
Paddington ™
"Surfing"
PB4
© Paddington & Co. Ltd. 1996
Licensed by ©COPYRIGHTS

Doulton *Number*		*Price*		
	U.S. $	*Can. $*	*U.K. £*	*Aust. $*
PB4	30.00	40.00	20.00	40.00

PB5
PADDINGTON GARDENING™

Designer:	Zoe Annand
Modeller:	Zoe Annand
Height:	4", 10.1 cm
Colour:	Blue jacket, red hat, green watering can, yellow and red bucket and spade
Issued:	1996 - 1998

Royal Doulton
Paddington ™
"Gardening"
PB5
© Paddington & Co. Ltd. 1996
Licensed by ©COPYRIGHTS

Doulton *Number*		*Price*		
	U.S. $	*Can. $*	*U.K. £*	*Aust. $*
PB5	30.00	40.00	20.00	40.00

PB6
PADDINGTON BATHTIME™

Designer:	Zoe Annand
Modeller:	Zoe Annand
Height:	3 ¼", 8.5 cm
Colour:	Blue coat, yellow hat, brown scrubbing brush, yellow duck, pink soap
Issued:	1996 - 1998

Royal Doulton
Paddington ™
"Bathtime"
PB6
© Paddington & Co. Ltd. 1996
Licensed by ©COPYRIGHTS

Doulton *Number*		*Price*		
	U.S. $	*Can. $*	*U.K. £*	*Aust. $*
PB6	30.00	40.00	20.00	40.00

PB7
PADDINGTON THE GOLFER™

Designer:	Zoe Annand
Modeller:	Zoe Annand
Height:	3 ¾", 9.5 cm
Colour:	White top, red and yellow sweater, red hat, green trousers, white shoes
Issued:	1996 - 1998

Royal Doulton
Paddington™
"The Golfer"
PB7
© Paddington & Co. Ltd. 1996
Licensed by ©OPYRIGHTS

Doulton Number	Price			
	U.S. $	Can. $	U.K. £	Aust. $
PB7	30.00	40.00	20.00	40.00

PB8
PADDINGTON THE MUSICIAN™

Designer:	Zoe Annand
Modeller:	Zoe Annand
Height:	3 ¾", 9.5 cm
Colour:	Black jacket, red waistcoat, brown trousers, brown violin, brass trumpet
Issued:	1996 - 1998

Royal Doulton
Paddington™
"The Musician"
PB8
© Paddington & Co. Ltd. 1996
Licensed by ©OPYRIGHTS

Doulton Number	Price			
	U.S. $	Can. $	U.K. £	Aust. $
PB8	30.00	40.00	20.00	40.00

PB9
PADDINGTON AT CHRISTMAS TIME™

Designer:	Zoe Annand
Modeller:	Zoe Annand
Height:	3 ½", 8.9 cm
Colour:	Red coat, blue boots, yellow sleigh
Issued:	1996 - 1998

Royal Doulton
Paddington™
"At Christmas Time"
PB9
© Paddington & Co. Ltd. 1996
Licensed by ©OPYRIGHTS

Doulton Number	Price			
	U.S. $	Can. $	U.K. £	Aust. $
PB9	30.00	40.00	20.00	40.00

PB10
PADDINGTON MARMALADE SANDWICH™

Designer:	Zoe Annand
Modeller:	Zoe Annand
Height:	3 ½", 8.9 cm
Colour:	Dark blue coat, yellow hat, green book, orange and white sandwiches
Issued:	1997 - 1998

Doulton Number	Price			
	U.S. $	*Can. $*	*U.K. £*	*Aust. $*
PB10	30.00	40.00	20.00	40.00

PB11
PADDINGTON GOING TO BED™

Designer:	Zoe Annand
Modeller:	Zoe Annand
Height:	3 ¾", 9.5 cm
Colour:	Turquoise, red and yellow pyjamas, red hat
Issued:	1997 - 1998

Doulton Number	Price			
	U.S. $	*Can. $*	*U.K. £*	*Aust. $*
PB11	30.00	40.00	20.00	40.00

PB12
PADDINGTON THE FISHERMAN™

Designer:	Zoe Annand
Modeller:	Zoe Annand
Height:	3 ½", 8.9 cm
Colour:	Dark blue hat and wellingtons, red jacket with yellow buttons
Issued:	1997 - 1998

Doulton Number	Price			
	U.S. $	*Can. $*	*U.K. £*	*Aust. $*
PB12	30.00	40.00	20.00	40.00

CERAMIC SERIES
1999 to date

PADDINGTON AT THE STATION™
Style Two

Modeller:	Warren Platt
Height:	3 ¼", 8.5 cm
Colour:	Brown bear, blue coat, red hat, grey sack, gold suitcase corners
Issued:	1999 in a special edition of 2,000
Series:	Gold edition

Doulton Number	Price			
	U.S. $	Can. $	U.K. £	Aust. $
—	—	—	75.00	—

Note: Commissioned by Paddington and Friends

THE PIG PROMENADE

THE PIG PROMENADE BACKSTAMPS

| BK-1. | **BESWICK WARE SCRIPT**
1993 to mid 1994 | BK-2. | **BESWICK CREST**
mid 1994 to present |

PP 1
JOHN THE CONDUCTOR™
(Vietnamese Pot Bellied Pig)

Designer:	Martyn Alcock
Height:	4 ¾", 12.1 cm
Colour:	Black jacket, black bowtie
Issued:	1993 - 1996

Beswick Ware
JOHN
PP 1

Back Stamp	Price U.S. $	Can. $	U.K. £	Aust. $
BK1	100.00	150.00	50.00	160.00
BK2	80.00	125.00	45.00	125.00

PP 2
MATTHEW THE TRUMPET PLAYER™
(Large White Pig)

Designer:	Amanda Hughes-Lubeck
Height:	5", 12.7 cm
Colour:	Light red waistcoat, black bowtie
Issued:	1993 - 1996

Beswick Ware
MATTHEW
PP 2

Back Stamp	Price U.S. $	Can. $	U.K. £	Aust. $
PPBS-1	100.00	150.00	50.00	160.00
PPBS-2	80.00	125.00	45.00	125.00

PP 3
DAVID THE FLUTE PLAYER™
(Tamworth Pig)

Designer:	Amanda Hughes-Lubeck
Height:	5 ¼", 13.3 cm
Colour:	Dark green waistcoat, black bowtie
Issued:	1993 - 1996

Beswick Ware
DAVID
PP 3

Back Stamp	Price U.S. $	Can. $	U.K. £	Aust. $
PPBS-1	100.00	150.00	50.00	160.00
PPBS-2	80.00	125.00	45.00	125.00

PP 4
ANDREW THE CYMBAL PLAYER™
(Gloucester Old Spotted Pig)

Designer:	Martyn Alcock
Height:	4 ¾", 12.1 cm
Colour:	Blue waistcoat, yellow cymbals, black bowtie
Issued:	1993 - 1996
Varieties:	Also called George, PP10

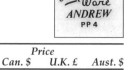

Back Stamp	Price			
	U.S. $	Can. $	U.K. £	Aust. $
PPBS-1	100.00	150.00	50.00	160.00
PPBS-2	80.00	125.00	45.00	125.00

PP 5
DANIEL THE VIOLINIST™
(Saddleback Pig)

Designer:	Amanda Hughes-Lubeck
Height:	5 ¼", 13.3 cm
Colour:	Pale blue waistcoat, brown violin
Issued:	1993 - 1996

Back Stamp	Price			
	U.S. $	Can. $	U.K. £	Aust. $
PPBS-1	100.00	150.00	50.00	160.00
PPBS-2	80.00	125.00	45.00	125.00

PP 6
MICHAEL THE BASS DRUM PLAYER™
(Large Black Pig)

Designer:	Martyn Alcock
Height:	4 ¾", 12.1 cm
Colour:	Yellow waistcoat, red and white drum
Issued:	1993 - 1996

Back Stamp	Price			
	U.S. $	Can. $	U.K. £	Aust. $
PPBS-1	100.00	150.00	50.00	160.00
PPBS-2	80.00	125.00	45.00	125.00

PP 7
JAMES THE TRIANGLE PLAYER™
(Tamworth Piglet)

Designer:	Warren Platt
Height:	4", 10.1 cm
Colour:	Tan, purple waistcoat, black bowtie
Issued:	1995 - 1996

Back Stamp	Price			
	U.S. $	Can. $	U.K. £	Aust. $
PPBS-2	90.00	125.00	45.00	125.00

PP 8
RICHARD THE FRENCH HORN PLAYER™

Designer:	Shane Ridge
Height:	5", 12.7 cm
Colour:	Pale pink with dark grey spots, tan and beige waistcoat
Issued:	1996 - 1996
Varieties:	Also called Benjamin, PP12

Back Stamp	Price			
	U.S. $	Can. $	U.K. £	Aust. $
PPBS-2	90.00	125.00	45.00	125.00

PP 9
CHRISTOPHER THE GUITAR PLAYER™

Designer:	Warren Platt
Height:	5 ½", 13.3 cm
Colour:	Dark grey, yellow and cream waistcoat, black bowtie
Issued:	1996 - 1996
Varieties:	Also called Thomas, PP11

Back Stamp	Price			
	U.S. $	Can. $	U.K. £	Aust. $
PPBS-2	90.00	125.00	40.00	125.00

PP 10
GEORGE™

Designer:	Martyn Alcock
Height:	4 ¾", 12.1 cm
Colour:	Dark green waistcoat, yellow cymbals, black bowtie
Issued:	1996 in a limited edition of 2,000
Varieties:	Also called Andrew, PP4

Back Stamp	Price			
	U.S. $	Can. $	U.K. £	Aust. $
PPBS-2	100.00	175.00	75.00	150.00

PP 11
THOMAS™

Designer:	Warren Platt
Height:	5", 12.7 cm
Colour:	Black pig with green jacket, yellow bowtie, white guitar
Issued:	1997 in a limited edition of 2,000
Varieties:	Also called Christopher the Guitar Player, PP9

Back Stamp	Price			
	U.S. $	Can. $	U.K. £	Aust. $
PPBS-2	100.00	175.00	75.00	175.00

PP 12
BENJAMIN™

Designer:	Shane Ridge
Height:	5", 12.7 cm
Colour:	White and black pig, orange bowtie, gold french horn
Issued:	1997 in a limited edition of 2,000
Varieties:	Also called Richard the French Horn Player, PP8

Back Stamp	Price			
	U.S. $	Can. $	U.K. £	Aust. $
PPBS-2	100.00	175.00	75.00	175.00

ST. TIGGYWINKLES

TW1
HENRY HEDGEHOG™
(Standing)

Designer: Unknown
Modeller: Amanda Hughes-Lubeck
Height: 3 ½", 8.5 cm
Colour: Light and dark brown hedgehog
               wearing a purple shirt
Issued: 1997 - 1999
Series: Wildlife Hospital Trust

| Doulton | Price | | | |
Number	U.S. $	Can. $	U.K. £	Aust. $
TW1	25.00	35.00	15.00	35.00

TW2
HARRY HEDGEHOG™
(Sitting)

Designer: Unknown
Modeller: Amanda Hughes-Lubeck
Height: 3 ½", 8.9 cm
Colour: Light and dark brown hedgehog
               wearing a purple shirt and red cap
Issued: 1997 - 1999
Series: Wildlife Hospital Trust

Royal Doulton
St. Tiggywinkles®
Harry Hedgehog
TW2/ *1269*
© St.Tiggywinkles 1996
Made in Thailand

| Doulton | Price | | | |
Number	U.S. $	Can. $	U.K. £	Aust. $
TW2	25.00	35.00	15.00	35.00

TW3
FRED FOX™

Designer: Unknown
Modeller: Warren Platt
Height: 4", 10.1 cm
Colour: Light brown fox wearing light blue
               overalls, pink shirt, white bandage
               around his head and tail
Issued: 1997 - 1998
Series: Wildlife Hospital Trust

Royal Doulton
St. Tiggywinkles®
Fred Fox
TW3/ *1094*
© St.Tiggywinkles 1996
Made in Thailand

| Doulton | Price | | | |
Number	U.S. $	Can. $	U.K. £	Aust. $
TW3	25.00	35.00	15.00	35.00

TW4
BOB BADGER™

Designer:	Unknown
Modeller:	Amanda Hughes-Lubeck
Height:	3 ¾", 9.5 cm
Colour:	Brown, black and white badger wearing a yellow jumper and brown scarf, beige crutch
Issued:	1997 - 1999
Series:	Wildlife Hospital Trust

Doulton Number	Price			
	U.S. $	Can. $	U.K. £	Aust. $
TW4	25.00	35.00	15.00	35.00

TW5
ROSIE RABBIT™

Designer:	Unknown
Modeller:	Amanda Hughes-Lubeck
Height:	3 ½", 8.9 cm
Colour:	Grey rabbit wearing a light blue dress and rose pinafore
Issued:	1997 - 1999
Series:	Wildlife Hospital Trust

Doulton Number	Price			
	U.S. $	Can. $	U.K. £	Aust. $
TW5	25.00	35.00	15.00	35.00

TW6
SARAH SQUIRREL™

Designer:	Unknown
Modeller:	Amanda Hughes-Lubeck
Height:	3 ¼", 8.3 cm
Colour:	Brown squirrel wearing a pink and white dress
Issued:	1997 - 1998
Series:	Wildlife Hospital Trust

Doulton Number	Price			
	U.S. $	Can. $	U.K. £	Aust. $
TW6	25.00	35.00	15.00	35.00

TW7
DANIEL DUCK™

Designer:	Unknown
Modeller:	Shane Ridge
Height:	3 ½", 8.5 cm
Colour:	Yellow duck, white and red bandage, brown satchel
Issued:	1997 - 1999
Series:	Wildlife Hospital Trust

Royal Doulton
St. Tiggywinkles
Daniel Duck
TW7/ **1925**
© St.Tiggywinkles 1996
Made in Thailand

Doulton Number	Price			
	U.S. $	Can. $	U.K. £	Aust. $
TW7	25.00	35.00	15.00	35.00

TW8
OLIVER OWL™

Designer:	Unknown
Modeller:	Warren Platt
Height:	4", 10.1 cm
Colour:	Dark and light brown owl, white arm sling, red book
Issued:	1997 - 1999
Series:	Wildlife Hospital Trust

Royal Doulton
St. Tiggywinkles
Oliver Owl
TW8/ **1703**
© St.Tiggywinkles 1996
Made in Thailand

Doulton Number	Price			
	U.S. $	Can. $	U.K. £	Aust. $
TW8	25.00	35.00	15.00	35.00

TW9
FRIENDS™

Designer:	Unknown
Modeller:	Amanda Hughes-Lubeck
Height:	4", 10.1 cm
Colour:	Brown hedgehog with green and yellow jacket, red hat, yellow ducks with blue scarf, white bandages
Issued:	1997 - 1999
Series:	Wildlife Hospital Trust

Royal Doulton
St. Tiggywinkles
Friends
TW9/ **1430**
© St.Tiggywinkles 1996
Made in Thailand

Doulton Number	Price			
	U.S. $	Can. $	U.K. £	Aust. $
TW9	35.00	50.00	20.00	50.00

TW10
A HELPING HAND™

Designer:	Unknown
Modeller:	Amanda Hughes-Lubeck
Height:	4", 10.1 cm
Colour:	Light and dark brown hedgehogs, white and grey rabbits, blue, yellow, pink and red clothing
Issued:	1997 - 1999
Series:	Wildlife Hospital Trust

Royal Doulton
St. Tiggywinkles®
A Helping Hand
TW10/ 0303
© St.Tiggywinkles 1996
Made in Thailand

Doulton Number	Price			
	U.S. $	Can. $	U.K. £	Aust. $
TW10	50.00	75.00	30.00	75.00

TW11
DEBORAH DORMOUSE™

Designer:	Unknown
Modeller:	Rob Simpson
Height:	3 ¼", 8.3 cm
Colour:	Brown dormouse wearing a pink dress, white apron, carrying a brown basket
Issued:	1998 - 1999
Series:	Wildlife Hospital Trust

Royal Doulton
St. Tiggywinkles®
Deborah Dormouse
TW11/ 458
© St.Tiggywinkles 1998
Made in Thailand

Doulton Number	Price			
	U.S. $	Can. $	U.K. £	Aust. $
TW11	25.00	35.00	15.00	35.00

TW12
MONTY MOLE™

Designer:	Unknown
Modeller:	Rob Simpson
Height:	3 ½", 8.5 cm
Colour:	Dark brown mole wearing a blue jacket, yellow hat, white arm sling
Issued:	1998 - 1999
Series:	Wildlife Hospital Trust

Doulton Number	Price			
	U.S. $	Can. $	U.K. £	Aust. $
TW12	25.00	35.00	15.00	35.00

TW13
FRANCHESCA FAWN™

Designer:	Unknown
Modeller:	Rob Simpson
Height:	3", 7.6 cm
Colour:	Pale brown fawn, white bandages
Issued:	1998 - 1999
Series:	Wildlife Hospital Trust

Royal Doulton
St. Tiggywinkles
Franchesca Fawn
TW13/48
© St.Tiggywinkles 1998
Made in Thailand

Doulton Number	Price			
	U.S. $	Can. $	U.K. £	Aust. $
TW13	25.00	35.00	15.00	35.00

THE SNOWMAN
GIFT COLLECTION

DS1
JAMES™
Style One

Designer:	Harry Sales
Modeller:	David Lyttleton
Height:	3 ¾", 9.5 cm
Colour:	Blue and white striped pyjamas, brown dressing gown
Issued:	1985 - 1993

Doulton Number	Price			
	U.S. $	*Can. $*	*U.K. £*	*Aust. $*
DS1	150.00	225.00	75.00	200.00

Royal Doulton®
THE SNOWMAN™
GIFT COLLECTION
JAMES
DS 1
© 1985 ROYAL DOULTON (UK)
© S ENT 1985

DS2
THE SNOWMAN™
Style One

Designer:	Harry Sales
Modeller:	David Lyttleton
Height:	5", 12.7 cm
Colour:	White snowman wearing a green hat and scarf
Issued:	1985 - 1994

Doulton Number	Price			
	U.S. $	*Can. $*	*U.K. £*	*Aust. $*
DS2	125.00	200.00	45.00	200.00

Royal Doulton®
THE SNOWMAN™
GIFT COLLECTION
THE SNOWMAN
DS 2
© 1985 ROYAL DOULTON (UK)
© S ENT 1985

DS3
STYLISH SNOWMAN™

Designer:	Harry Sales
Modeller:	David Lyttleton
Height:	5", 12.7 cm
Colour:	White snowman wearing blue trousers, lilac braces, grey hat, yellow tie with red stripes
Issued:	1985 - 1993

Doulton Number	Price			
	U.S. $	*Can. $*	*U.K. £*	*Aust. $*
DS3	150.00	225.00	85.00	200.00

Royal Doulton®
THE SNOWMAN™
GIFT COLLECTION
STYLISH SNOWMAN
DS 3
© 1985 ROYAL DOULTON (UK)
© S ENT 1985

DS4
THANK YOU SNOWMAN™

Designer:	Harry Sales
Modeller:	David Lyttleton
Height:	5", 12.7 cm
Colour:	Snowman - green hat and scarf
	James - brown dressing gown
Issued:	1985 - 1994

Doulton Number	Price			
	U.S. $	Can. $	U.K. £	Aust. $
DS4	100.00	150.00	50.00	150.00

DS5
SNOWMAN MAGIC MUSIC BOX™

Designer:	Harry Sales
Modeller:	David Lyttleton
Height:	8", 20.3 cm
Colour:	White snowman wearing a green hat and scarf, cream music box with blue, green and pink balloon design
Issued:	1985 - 1994
Tune:	Walking in the Air

Doulton Number	Price			
	U.S. $	Can. $	U.K. £	Aust. $
DS5	175.00	275.00	100.00	250.00

DS6
COWBOY SNOWMAN™

Designer:	Harry Sales
Modeller:	David Lyttleton
Height:	5", 12.7 cm
Colour:	White snowman wearing a brown hat and holster belt
Issued:	1986 - 1992

Doulton Number	Price			
	U.S. $	Can. $	U.K. £	Aust. $
DS6	275.00	400.00	175.00	375.00

DS7
HIGHLAND SNOWMAN™

Designer:	Harry Sales
Modeller:	David Lyttleton
Height:	5 ¼", 13.3 cm
Colour:	White snowman wearing a red, blue and white kilt
Issued:	1987 - 1993

Royal Doulton®
THE SNOWMAN™
GIFT COLLECTION
HIGHLAND SNOWMAN
DS 7
© 1985 ROYAL DOULTON (UK)
© S ENT 1985

Doulton Number	Price			
	U.S. $	Can. $	U.K. £	Aust. $
DS7	225.00	350.00	125.00	325.00

DS8
LADY SNOWMAN™

Designer:	Harry Sales
Modeller:	David Lyttleton
Height:	5", 12.7 cm
Colour:	White snowman wearing a pink apron and blue hat
Issued:	1987 - 1992

Royal Doulton®
THE SNOWMAN™
GIFT COLLECTION
LADY SNOWMAN
DS 8
© 1985 ROYAL DOULTON (UK)
© S ENT 1985

Doulton Number	Price			
	U.S. $	Can. $	U.K. £	Aust. $
DS8	450.00	550.00	200.00	500.00

DS9
BASS DRUMMER SNOWMAN™

Designer:	Graham Tongue
Modeller:	Warren Platt
Height:	5 ¼", 13.3 cm
Colour:	White snowman with pale blue hat, pink and yellow drum, pale brown straps
Issued:	1987 - 1993

Royal Doulton®
THE SNOWMAN™
GIFT COLLECTION
BASS DRUMMER SNOWMAN
DS 9
© 1987 ROYAL DOULTON
© S ENT 1987

Doulton Number	Price			
	U.S. $	Can. $	U.K. £	Aust. $
DS9	450.00	500.00	150.00	475.00

DS10
FLAUTIST SNOWMAN™

Designer:	Graham Tongue
Modeller:	Warren Platt
Height:	5 ½", 14.0 cm
Colour:	White snowman wearing a yellow and red cap and a brown tie
Issued:	1987 - 1993

Doulton Number	Price			
	U.S. $	Can. $	U.K. £	Aust. $
DS10	225.00	400.00	150.00	350.00

DS11
VIOLINIST SNOWMAN™

Designer:	Graham Tongue
Modeller:	Warren Platt
Height:	5 ¼", 13.3 cm
Colour:	White snowman wearing a green waistcoat with yellow collar, blue bowtie, brown cap, playing a violin
Issued:	1987 - 1994

Doulton Number	Price			
	U.S. $	Can. $	U.K. £	Aust. $
DS11	100.00	150.00	50.00	150.00

DS12
PIANIST SNOWMAN™

Designer:	Graham Tongue
Modeller:	Warren Platt
Height:	5", 12.7 cm
Colour:	White snowman wearing a blue crown and orange tie
Issued:	1987 - 1994

Doulton Number	Price			
	U.S. $	Can. $	U.K. £	Aust. $
DS12	100.00	150.00	50.00	165.00

DS13
SNOWMAN'S PIANO™

Designer:	Graham Tongue
Modeller:	Warren Platt
Height:	5 ¼", 13.3 cm
Colour:	White piano
Issued:	1987 - 1994

Royal Doulton®
THE SNOWMAN™
GIFT COLLECTION
SNOWMAN'S PIANO
D S 13
© 1987 ROYAL DOULTON
© S. ENT 1987

Doulton Number	Price			
	U.S. $	Can. $	U.K. £	Aust. $
DS13	60.00	100.00	30.00	125.00

DS14
CYMBAL PLAYER SNOWMAN™

Designer:	Graham Tongue
Modeller:	Warren Platt
Height:	5 ¼", 13.3 cm
Colour:	White snowman wearing a brown waistcoat, green cap and bowtie, playing yellow cymbals
Issued:	1988 - 1993

Royal Doulton®
THE SNOWMAN™
GIFT COLLECTION
CYMBAL PLAYER SNOWMAN
D S 14
© 1988 ROYAL DOULTON
© S ENT 1988

Doulton Number	Price			
	U.S. $	Can. $	U.K. £	Aust. $
DS14	300.00	400.00	150.00	375.00

DS15
DRUMMER SNOWMAN™

Designer:	Graham Tongue
Modeller:	Warren Platt
Height:	5 ¾", 14.6 cm
Colour:	White snowman wearing a red and black hat, purple bowtie, playing pink and yellow drum
Issued:	1988 - 1994

Royal Doulton®
THE SNOWMAN™
GIFT COLLECTION
DRUMMER SNOWMAN
D S 15
© 1988 ROYAL DOULTON
© S ENT 1988

Doulton Number	Price			
	U.S. $	Can. $	U.K. £	Aust. $
DS15	150.00	200.00	75.00	200.00

DS16
TRUMPETER SNOWMAN™

Designer: Graham Tongue
Modeller: Warren Platt
Height: 5", 12.7 cm
Colour: White snowman wearing a pink
             hat playing a yellow trumpet
Issued: 1988 - 1993

Doulton Number	Price			
	U.S. $	Can. $	U.K. £	Aust. $
DS16	300.00	400.00	150.00	375.00

DS17
CELLIST SNOWMAN™

Designer: Graham Tongue
Modeller: Warren Platt
Height: 5 ¼", 13.3 cm
Colour: White snowman wearing a
             green waistcoat with yellow
             collar, blue bowtie, playing
             a brown cello
Issued: 1988 - 1993

Doulton Number	Price			
	U.S. $	Can. $	U.K. £	Aust. $
DS17	150.00	175.00	60.00	175.00

DS18
SNOWMAN MUSICAL BOX™

Designer: Unknown
Height: 8", 22.5 cm
Colour: White snowman wearing a red, blue
             and white kilt, green, pink and blue
             balloons on box
Issued: 1988 - 1990
Tune: Blue Bells of Scotland

Doulton Numbers	Price			
	U.S. $	Can. $	U.K. £	Aust. $
DS18	275.00	350.00	125.00	300.00

DS19
SNOWMAN MONEY BOX™

Designer:	Graham Tongue
Modeller:	Warren Platt
Height:	8 ½", 21.6 cm
Colour:	White snowman wearing a green hat with grey band and green scarf
Issued:	1990 - 1994

Doulton Number	Price			
	U.S. $	Can. $	U.K. £	Aust. $
DS19	200.00	300.00	100.00	275.00

DS20
THE SNOWMAN TOBOGGANING™

Designer:	Graham Tongue
Modeller:	Warren Platt
Height:	5", 12.7 cm
Colour:	White snowman wearing a green hat and scarf, rose-pink toboggan
Issued:	1990 - 1994

Royal Doulton ®
THE SNOWMAN ™
GIFT COLLECTION
THE SNOWMAN
TOBOGGANING
DS 20
© 1990 ROYAL DOULTON
© S ENT 1990

Doulton Number	Price			
	U.S. $	Can. $	U.K. £	Aust. $
DS20	150.00	250.00	75.00	250.00

DS21
THE SNOWMAN SKIING™

Designer:	Graham Tongue
Modeller:	Warren Platt
Height:	5", 12.7 cm
Colour:	White snowman wearing a green hat and scarf, yellow and black goggles
Issued:	1990 - 1992

Royal Doulton ®
THE SNOWMAN ™
GIFT COLLECTION
THE SNOWMAN
SKIING
DS 21
© 1990 ROYAL DOULTON
© S ENT 1990

Doulton Number	Price			
	U.S. $	Can. $	U.K. £	Aust. $
DS21	700.00	1,000.00	400.00	1,000.00

DS22
THE SNOWMAN SNOWBALLING™

Designer:	Graham Tongue
Modeller:	Warren Platt
Height:	5", 12.7 cm
Colour:	White snowman wearing a green hat and scarf, brown tree stump
Issued:	1990 - 1994

Doulton Number	Price			
	U.S. $	Can. $	U.K. £	Aust. $
DS22	150.00	250.00	60.00	225.00

DS23
BUILDING THE SNOWMAN™

Designer:	Graham Tongue
Modeller:	Warren Platt
Height:	4", 10.1 cm
Colour:	White snowman wearing a green hat and scarf
Issued:	1990 - 1994

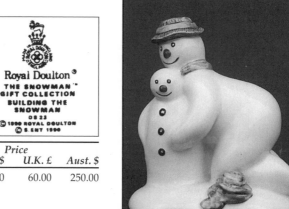

Doulton Number	Price			
	U.S. $	Can. $	U.K. £	Aust. $
DS23	150.00	250.00	60.00	250.00

D6972
SNOWMAN MINIATURE
CHARACTER JUG™

Designer:	Graham Tongue
Modeller:	Martyn Alcock
Height:	2 ¾", 7.0 cm
Colour:	White snowman wearing a black hat, green scarf forms the handle
Issued:	1994 - 1994

Doulton Number	Price			
	U.S. $	Can. $	U.K. £	Aust. $
D6972	175.00	200.00	100.00	225.00

JAMES™
Style Two

Designer:	Shane Ridge	
Modeller:	Shane Ridge	
Height:	4 ¼", 10.8 cm	
Colour:	Brown dressing gown, white and blue striped pyjamas	
Issued:	1999 in a limited edition of 2,500	

Doulton Number		Price			
		U.S. $	Can. $	U.K. £	Aust. $
—		—	—	50.00	—

Note: Issued as a pair with The Snowman (Style Two).

JAMES™ (James Build a Snowman)
Style Three

Designer:	Shane Ridge
Modeller:	Shane Ridge
Height:	4", 10.1 cm
Colour:	Maroon sweater, blue trousers, black wellingtons
Issued:	2000 in a limited edition of 2,500

Doulton Number		Price			
		U.S. $	Can. $	U.K. £	Aust. $
—	Pair with The Snowman (Style Three)	—	—	99.75	—

Note: Issued, numbered and sold as a pair with The Snowman (Style Three).

THE SNOWMAN™
Style Two

Designer:	Shane Ridge
Modeller:	Shane Ridge
Height:	5 ¾", 14.6 cm
Colour:	White snowman, green hat and scarf
Issued:	1999 in a limited edition of 2,500

Doulton Number		Price			
		U.S. $	Can. $	U.K. £	Aust. $
—		—	—	50.00	—

Note: Issued as a pair with James (Style Two).

THE SNOWMAN™ (James Builds a Snowman)
Style Three

Designer:	Shane Ridge				
Modeller:	Shane Ridge				
Height:	6", 15.0 cm				
Colour:	White and green				
Issued:	2000 in a limited edition of 2,500				

Doulton Number		U.S. $	Can. $	*Price* U.K. £	Aust. $
—	Pair with James (Style Three)	—	—	99.75	—

Note: Issued, numbered and sold as a pair with James (Style Three).

DANCING IN THE SNOW™

Designer:	Shane Ridge				
Modeller:	Shane Ridge				
Height:	5 ¾", 14.6 cm				
Colour:	Snowman: White, black buttons, yellow scarf				
	James: Brown dressing gown, blue and white striped pyjamas				
Issued:	1999 in a limited edition of 2,500				
Series:	Tableau				

Doulton Number	U.S. $	Can. $	*Price* U.K. £	Aust. $
—	—	—	99.75	—

Note: Issued to commemorate the 21st Anniversary of Raymond Briggs' Tale.

SNOWMAN AND JAMES
THE ADVENTURE BEGINS™

Designer:	Shane Ridge				
Modeller:	Shane Ridge				
Height:	6", 15.0 cm				
Colour:	White, green, brown and blue				
Issued:	2000 in a limited edition of 2,500				
Series:	Tableau				

Doulton Number	U.S. $	Can. $	*Price* U.K. £	Aust. $
—	—	—	110.00	—

SPORTING
CHARACTERS

SC1
FLY FISHING

Designer:	Andy Moss
Height:	3 ¼", 8.3 cm
Colour:	Green, slate, blue and black
Issued:	1998 in a limited edition of 1,500
Series:	Sporting Characters

Beswick	Price			
Number	U.S. $	Can. $	U.K. £	Aust. $
SC1	65.00	100.00	40.00	100.00

SC2
LAST LION OF DEFENCE

Designer:	Andy Moss
Height:	4 ¼", 10.8 cm
Colour:	Red and white
Issued:	1998 in a limited edition of 1,500
Series:	Sporting Characters

Beswick	Price			
Number	U.S. $	Can. $	U.K. £	Aust. $
SC2	65.00	100.00	40.00	100.00

SC3
IT'S A KNOCKOUT

Designer:	Andy Moss
Height:	4 ¼", 10.8 cm
Colour:	Red, white and black
Issued:	1998 in a limited edition of 1,500
Series:	Sporting Characters

Beswick	Price			
Number	U.S. $	Can. $	U.K. £	Aust. $
SC3	65.00	100.00	40.00	100.00

SC4
SLOPING OFF

Designer:	Andy Moss
Height:	5 ¼", 13.3 cm
Colour:	White, black and yellow
Issued:	1999 in a special edition of 1,500
Series:	Sporting Characters

Beswick Number	Price			
	U.S. $	Can. $	U.K. £	Aust. $
SC4	65.00	100.00	40.00	100.00

SC5
A ROUND WITH FOXY

Designer:	Andy Moss
Height:	6", 15.0 cm
Colour:	Green, yellow and brown
Issued:	2000 in a special edition of 1,500
Series:	Sporting Characters

Beswick Number	Price			
	U.S. $	Can. $	U.K. £	Aust. $
SC5	65.00	100.00	40.00	100.00

SC6
OUT FOR A DUCK

Designer:	Andy Moss
Height:	5 ½", 14.0 cm
Colour:	Cream
Issued:	2000 in a special edition of 1,500
Series:	Sporting Characters

Beswick Number	Price			
	U.S. $	Can. $	U.K. £	Aust. $
SC6	65.00	100.00	40.00	100.00

THUNDERBIRDS

3337
LADY PENELOPE™

Designer:	William K. Harper
Height:	4", 10.1 cm
Colour:	Pink hat and coat, blonde hair
Issued:	1992 in a limited edition of 2,500

Beswick Number	Price U.S. $	Can. $	U.K. £	Aust. $
3337	145.00	225.00	95.00	240.00
Complete set of 6 figures	700.00	1,000.00	450.00	1,200.00

3339
BRAINS™

Designer:	William K. Harper
Height:	4", 10.1 cm
Colour:	Black and blue uniform, blue glasses, black hair
Issued:	1992 in a limited edition of 2,500

Beswick Number	Price U.S. $	Can. $	U.K. £	Aust. $
3339	135.00	200.00	85.00	225.00

3344
SCOTT TRACY™

Designer:	William K. Harper
Height:	4", 10.1 cm
Colour:	Blue uniform, light blue band
Issued:	1992 in a limited edition of 2,500

Beswick Number	Price U.S. $	Can. $	U.K. £	Aust. $
3344	145.00	225.00	95.00	240.00

3345
VIRGIL TRACY™

Designer:	William K. Harper
Height:	4", 10.1 cm
Colour:	Blue uniform, yellow band
Issued:	1992 in a limited edition of 2,500

Beswick Number	Price			
	U.S. $	Can. $	U.K. £	Aust. $
3345	135.00	200.00	85.00	225.00

3346
PARKER™

Designer:	William K. Harper
Height:	4", 10.1 cm
Colour:	Blue-grey uniform
Issued:	1992 in a limited edition of 2,500

Beswick Number	Price			
	U.S. $	Can. $	U.K. £	Aust. $
3346	125.00	200.00	80.00	225.00

3348
THE HOOD™

Designer:	William K. Harper
Height:	4", 10.1 cm
Colour:	Browns
Issued:	1992 in a limited edition of 2,500

Beswick Number	Price			
	U.S. $	Can. $	U.K. £	Aust. $
3348	125.00	200.00	80.00	225.00

John Beswick
by Royal Doulton

THUNDERBIRDS

This collection of hand-made, hand-decorated ceramic busts, modelled by William K. Harper, is issued in a limited edition of two thousand five hundred.

No.

104

© 1992 John Beswick © 1992 ITC Entertainment Group Ltd. Licensed by Copyright Promotions Ltd.

TURNER ENTERTAINMENT

3547
DROOPY™

Designer:	Simon Ward
Height:	4 ½", 11.4 cm
Colour:	White dog with black ears, red cap
Issued:	1995 in a special edition of 2,000

Beswick	Price			
Number	*U.S. $*	*Can. $*	*U.K. £*	*Aust. $*
3547	50.00	75.00	35.00	75.00

3549
JERRY™

Designer:	Simon Ward
Height:	3", 7.6 cm
Colour	Red-brown and cream mouse, white base
Issued:	1995 in special edition of 2,000

Beswick	Price			
Number	*U.S. $*	*Can. $*	*U.K. £*	*Aust. $*
3549	50.00	75.00	35.00	75.00

3552
TOM™

Designer:	Simon Ward
Height:	4 ½", 11.4 cm
Colour:	Grey-blue and pink cat, white base
Issued:	1995 in a special edition of 2,000

Beswick	Price			
Number	*U.S. $*	*Can. $*	*U.K. £*	*Aust. $*
3552	50.00	75.00	35.00	75.00

THE WIZARD OF OZ™

3709
SCARECROW™

Designer:	Andy Moss
Height:	6 ½", 16.5 cm
Colour:	Black hat and shirt, brown pants and shoes
Issued:	1998 in a special edition of 1,500
Series:	The Wizard of Oz

Doulton Number	Price U.S. $	Can. $	U.K. £	Aust. $
3709	125.00	175.00	75.00	200.00
Set of 4 figures	450.00	625.00	285.00	700.00

3731
LION™

Designer:	Andy Moss
Height:	6", 15.0 cm
Colour:	Light and dark brown
Issued:	1998 in a special edition of 1,500
Series:	The Wizard of Oz

Doulton Number	Price U.S. $	Can. $	U.K. £	Aust. $
3731	125.00	175.00	75.00	200.00

3732
DOROTHY™

Designer:	Andy Moss
Height:	5", 12.7 cm
Colour:	Blue and white dress, red shoes, black dog
Issued:	1998 in a special edition of 1,500
Series:	The Wizard of Oz

Doulton		*Price*		
Number	*U.S. $*	*Can. $*	*U.K. £*	*Aust. $*
3732	125.00	175.00	75.00	200.00

3738
TINMAN™

Designer:	Andy Moss
Height:	7", 17.8 cm
Colour:	Grey
Issued:	1998 in a special edition of 1,500
Series:	The Wizard of Oz

Doulton		*Price*		
Number	*U.S. $*	*Can. $*	*U.K. £*	*Aust. $*
3738	125.00	175.00	75.00	200.00

20TH CENTURY ADVERTISING CLASSICS

AC 1
FATHER WILLIAM™

Modeller:	William K. Harper
Height:	6 ¼", 15.9 cm
Colour:	Black jacket and shoes, yellow checked trousers, red waistcoat and cane, grey top hat
Issued:	1999 in a limited edition of 2,000
Slogan:	Get YOUNGER every day

Back Stamp	Price			
	U.S. $	Can. $	U.K. £	Aust. $
AC 1	—	—	85.00	—

AC 2
GOLLY™

Modeller:	William K. Harper
Height:	5 ½", 14.0 cm
Colour:	Blue jacket, red trousers, orange waistcoat, red and white bow tie
Issued:	1999 in a limited edition of 2,000
Slogan:	Golly it's Good!

Back Stamp	Price			
	U.S. $	Can. $	U.K. £	Aust. $
AC 2	—	—	90.00	—

AC 3
SIR KREEMY KNUT™
(Sharps Toffee - Trebor Bassett Ltd)

Modeller:	William K. Harper
Height:	6 ¼", 15.9 cm
Colour:	Blue suit, white shirt, red bow tie, black hat, brown shoes
Issued:	1999 in a limited edition of 2,000
Slogan:	Sharps the word for Toffee!

Back Stamp	Price			
	U.S. $	Can. $	U.K. £	Aust. $
AC 3	—	—	75.00	—

AC 4
FOX'S POLAR BEAR™
(Fox's Glacier Mints - Nestlé)

Modeller:	William K. Harper
Height:	4 ¼", 10.8 cm
Colour:	White
Issued:	1999 in a limited edition of 2,000
Slogan:	FOX

Back Stamp	U.S. $	Can. $	Price U.K. £	Aust. $
AC 4	—	—	75.00	—

AC 5
PLAYER'S 'HERO' SAILOR™
(John Player & Sons Ltd - Imperial Tobacco Ltd)

Modeller:	William K. Harper
Height:	6", 15.0 cm
Colour:	Navy and white sailor suit and life buoy
Issued:	1999 in a limited edition of 2,000
Slogan:	Player's Please

Back Stamp	U.S. $	Can. $	Price U.K. £	Aust. $
AC 5	—	—	80.00	—

AC 6
JOHN GINGER™
(Huntley & Palmers - The Jacobs Bakery Ltd)

Modeller:	William K. Harper
Height:	6", 15.0 cm
Colour:	Dark green jacket and trousers, white collar and cuffs, black belt, shoes and hat, yellow buckle and stockings
Issued:	2000 in a limited edition of 2,000

Back Stamp	U.S. $	Can. $	Price U.K. £	Aust. $
AC 6	—	—	75.00	—

AC 7
THE MILKY BAR KID™
(Nestlé)

Modeller:	William K. Harper
	David Biggs
Height:	5", 12.7 cm
Colour:	Blue shirt, red trousers, brown vest and
	boots, white hat
Issued:	2000 in a limited edition of 2,000
Slogan:	The Milkybars are on me!

Back Stamp	Price			
	U.S. $	Can. $	U.K. £	Aust. $
AC 7	—	—	75.00	—

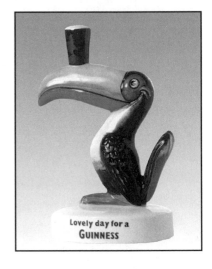

AC 8
GUINNESS TOUCAN™
(©Guinness Ltd)

Modeller:	William K. Harper
Height:	6", 15.0 cm
Colour:	Black, white, blue and orange
Issued:	2000 in a limited edition of 2,000
Slogan:	Lovely day for a GUINNESS

Back Stamp	Price			
	U.S. $	Can. $	U.K. £	Aust. $
AC 8	—	—	85.00	—

WALT DISNEY

101 DALMATIANS
DISNEY CHARACTERS
DISNEY PRINCESS COLLECTION
DISNEY SHOWCASE COLLECTION
DISNEY VILLAINS COLLECTION
FANTASIA 2000
FILM CLASSICS COLLECTION
MICKEY MOUSE COLLECTION
PETER PAN
SNOW WHITE AND THE SEVEN DWARFS
WINNIE THE POOH

101 DALMATIANS
1997 to the present

DM 1
CRUELLA DE VIL™
Style One

Designer:	Martyn Alcock
Modeller:	Martyn Alcock
Height:	6 ¼", 15.9 cm
Colour:	Black dress, pale yellow coat with red lining and gloves
Issued:	1997 to the present
Series:	101 Dalmatians Collection

Royal Doulton®
DISNEY'S
101 DALMATIANS
CRUELLA DE VIL
DM 1
© Disney

Doulton Number	Price			
	U.S. $	Can. $	U.K. £	Aust. $
DM 1	150.00	200.00	87.50	200.00

DM 2
PENNY™

Designer:	Shane Ridge
Modeller:	Shane Ridge
Height:	2 ¾", 7.0 cm
Colour:	White and black dalmatian, red collar
Issued:	1997 to the present
Series:	101 Dalmatians Collection

Royal Doulton®
DISNEY'S
101 DALMATIANS
PENNY
DM 2
© Disney

Doulton Number	Price			
	U.S. $	Can. $	U.K. £	Aust. $
DM 2	—	—	21.00	—

DM 3
PENNY™ AND FRECKLES™

Designer:	Martyn Alcock
Modeller:	Martyn Alcock
Height:	2 ¼", 5.5 cm
Colour:	Two white and black dalmatians with red collars
Issued:	1997 to the present
Series:	101 Dalmatians Collection

Royal Doulton®
DISNEY'S
101 DALMATIANS
PENNY AND FRECKLES
DM 3
© Disney

Doulton Number	Price			
	U.S. $	Can. $	U.K. £	Aust. $
DM 3	—	—	25.50	—

DM 4
ROLLY™

Designer:	Shane Ridge
Modeller:	Shane Ridge
Height:	2 ¾", 7.0 cm
Colour:	White and black dalmatian, red collar, black base
Issued:	1997 - 1999
Series:	101 Dalmatians Collection

Doulton Number	Price			
	U.S. $	Can. $	U.K. £	Aust. $
DM 4	40.00	50.00	20.00	45.00

DM 5
PATCH™, ROLLY™ AND FRECKLES™

Designer:	Shane Ridge
Modeller:	Shane Ridge
Height:	3 ¾", 9.5 cm
Length:	7 ½", 19.0 cm
Colour:	Three white and black dalmatians wearing red collars
Issued:	1997 in a limited edition of 3,500
Series:	1. 101 Dalmatians Collection 2. Tableau

Doulton Number	Price			
	U.S. $	Can. $	U.K. £	Aust. $
DM 5	300.00	425.00	175.00	425.00

DM 6
PONGO™

Designer:	Martyn Alcock
Modeller:	Martyn Alcock
Height:	4 ½", 11.9 cm
Colour:	White and black dalmatian, red collar
Issued:	1997 - 1998
Series:	101 Dalmatians Collection

Doulton Number	Price			
	U.S. $	Can. $	U.K. £	Aust. $
DM 6	45.00	60.00	26.00	65.00

DM 7
PERDITA™

Designer:	Martyn Alcock
Modeller:	Martyn Alcock
Height:	2 ½", 6.4 cm
Colour:	White and black dalmatian, dark turquoise collar and blanket
Issued:	1997 to the present
Series:	101 Dalmatians Collection

Royal Doulton®
DISNEY'S
101 DALMATIANS
PERDITA
DM 7
© Disney

Doulton Number	Price			
	U.S. $	Can. $	U.K. £	Aust. $
DM 7	—	—	25.50	—

DM 8
LUCKY™

Designer:	Martyn Alcock
Modeller:	Martyn Alcock
Height:	2 ¾", 7.0 cm
Colour:	White and black dalmatian, red collar
Issued:	1997 to the present
Series:	101 Dalmatians Collection

Royal Doulton®
DISNEY'S
101 DALMATIANS
LUCKY DM 8
© Disney

Doulton Number	Price			
	U.S. $	Can. $	U.K. £	Aust. $
DM 8	—	—	21.00	—

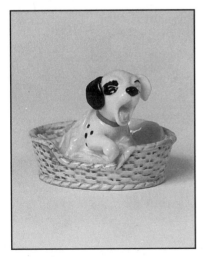

DM 9
PATCH™ IN BASKET

Designer:	Graham Tongue
Modeller:	Graham Tongue
Height:	2 ¼", 5.7 cm
Colour:	White and black dalmatian, beige basket
Issued:	1998 to the present
Series:	101 Dalmatians Collection

DISNEY'S
101 DALMATIANS
PATCH IN BASKET
DM 9
Royal Doulton® © Disney

Doulton Number	Price			
	U.S. $	Can. $	U.K. £	Aust. $
DM 9	—	—	23.00	—

DM 10
LUCKY™ AND FRECKLES™ ON ICE

Designer:	Warren Platt
Modeller:	Warren Platt
Height:	2 ½", 6.4 cm
Colour:	White and black dalmatians
Issued:	1998 - 1999
Series:	101 Dalmatians Collection

Doulton Number	Price			
	U.S. $	Can. $	U.K. £	Aust. $
DM 10	125.00	200.00	75.00	200.00

DM 11
PUPS IN THE CHAIR™

Designer:	Martyn Alcock
Modeller:	Martyn Alcock
Height:	4", 10.1 cm
Colour:	White and black dalmatians, yellow chair
Issued:	February 1st to May 12th, 1999 (101 days)
Series:	101 Dalmatians Collection

Doulton Number	Price			
	U.S. $	Can. $	U.K. £	Aust. $
DM 11	175.00	300.00	100.00	200.00

DISNEY CHARACTERS

1952-1965

1278
MICKEY MOUSE™
Style One

Designer: Jan Granoska
Height: 4", 10.1 cm
Colour: Black, white and red
Issued: 1952 - 1965

Back Stamp	Beswick Number	Price			
		U.S. $	Can. $	U.K. £	Aust. $
Beswick Gold	1278	1,000.00	1,200.00	500.00	1,200.00

1279
JIMINY CRICKET™
Style One

Designer: Jan Granoska
Height: 4", 10.1 cm
Colour: Black, white, beige and blue
Issued: 1952 - 1965

Back Stamp	Beswick Number	Price			
		U.S. $	Can. $	U.K. £	Aust. $
Beswick Gold	1279	675.00	875.00	400.00	900.00

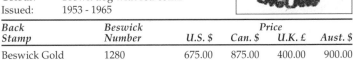

1280
PLUTO™
Style One

Designer: Jan Granoska
Height: 3 ½", 8.9 cm
Colour: Brown dog with red collar
Issued: 1953 - 1965

Back Stamp	Beswick Number	Price			
		U.S. $	Can. $	U.K. £	Aust. $
Beswick Gold	1280	675.00	875.00	400.00	900.00

1281
GOOFY™
Style One

Designer:	Jan Granoska
Height:	4 ¼", 10.8 cm
Colour:	Red jersey, blue trousers, black suspenders, white gloves, brown and black hat, brown boots
Issued:	1953 - 1965

Back Stamp	Beswick Number	Price			
		U.S. $	Can. $	U.K. £	Aust. $
Beswick Gold	1281	675.00	900.00	400.00	1,000.00

1282
PINOCCHIO™
Style One

Designer:	Jan Granoska
Height:	4", 10.1 cm
Colour:	White and yellow jacket, red trousers, blue bowtie and shoes, brown cap
Issued:	1953 - 1965

Back Stamp	Beswick Number	Price			
		U.S. $	Can. $	U.K. £	Aust. $
Beswick Gold	1282	775.00	1,000.00	525.00	1,100.00

1283
DONALD DUCK™
Style One

Designer:	Jan Granoska
Height:	4", 10.1 cm
Colour:	White duck, blue sailors jacket, red bow, blue and black hat
Issued:	1953 - 1965

Back Stamp	Beswick Number	Price			
		U.S. $	Can. $	U.K. £	Aust. $
Beswick Gold	1283	775.00	1,000.00	450.00	1,100.00

1289
MINNIE MOUSE™
Style One

Designer:	Jan Granoska
Height:	4", 10.1 cm
Colour:	Black and white mouse wearing a yellow top and red skirt with white spots, white gloves and hair bow, brown shoes
Issued:	1953 - 1965

Back Stamp	Beswick Number	Price U.S. $	Can. $	U.K. £	Aust. $
Beswick Gold	1289	750.00	1,000.00	450.00	1,100.00

1291
THUMPER™
Style One

Designer:	Jan Granoska
Height:	3 ¾", 9.5 cm
Colour:	Grey and white rabbit, yellow, red and pink flowers on brown base
Issued:	1953 - 1965

Back Stamp	Beswick Number	Price U.S. $	Can. $	U.K. £	Aust. $
Beswick Gold	1291	525.00	650.00	275.00	625.00

THE DISNEY PRINCESS COLLECTION
1995-1996

HN 3677
CINDERELLA™

Designer:	Pauline Parsons
Height:	8", 20.3 cm
Colour:	Blue and white dress, yellow hair
Issued:	1995 in a limited edition of 2,000
Series:	The Disney Princess Collection

Back Stamp	Doulton Number	Price			
		U.S. $	Can. $	U.K. £	Aust. $
Doulton	HN 3677	400.00	600.00	200.00	550.00

HN 3678
SNOW WHITE™
Style Two

Designer:	Pauline Parsons
Height:	8 ¼", 21.0 cm
Colour:	Yellow, blue and white dress, royal blue and red cape, black hair
Issued:	1995 in a limited edition of 2,000
Series:	The Disney Princess Collection

Back Stamp	Doulton Number	Price			
		U.S. $	Can. $	U.K. £	Aust. $
Doulton	HN 3678	500.00	750.00	325.00	800.00

HN 3830
BELLE™

Designer:	Pauline Parsons
Height:	8", 20.3 cm
Colour:	Yellow dress and gloves, brown hair
Issued:	1996 in a limited edition of 2,000
Series:	The Disney Princess Collection

Back Stamp	Doulton Number	Price			
		U.S. $	Can. $	U.K. £	Aust. $
Doulton	HN 3830	400.00	600.00	200.00	600.00

HN 3831
ARIEL™

Designer:	Pauline Parsons
Height:	8 ¼", 21.0 cm
Colour:	White dress and veil, red hair
Issued:	1996 in a limited edition of 2,000
Series:	The Disney Princess Collection

Back Stamp	Doulton Number	Price			
		U.S. $	Can. $	U.K. £	Aust. $
Doulton	HN 3831	400.00	600.00	200.00	650.00

HN 3832
JASMINE™

Designer:	Pauline Parsons
Height:	7 ½", 19.1 cm
Colour:	Lilac dress
Issued:	1996 in a limited edition of 2,000
Series:	The Disney Princess Collection

Back Stamp	Doulton Number	Price			
		U.S. $	Can. $	U.K. £	Aust. $
Doulton	HN 3832	400.00	600.00	200.00	650.00

HN 3833
AURORA™

Designer:	Pauline Parsons
Height:	7 ½", 19.1 cm
Colour:	Light and dark blue dress with white trim
Issued:	1996 in a limited edition of 2,000
Series:	The Disney Princess Collection

Back Stamp	Doulton Number	Price			
		U.S. $	Can. $	U.K. £	Aust. $
Doulton	HN 3833	350.00	500.00	175.00	525.00

DISNEY SHOWCASE COLLECTION
JUNGLE BOOK

JB1
MOWGLI™

Designer:	Shane Ridge
Modeller:	Shane Ridge
Height:	2 ½", 6.4 cm
Colour:	Fleshtones, black and red
Issued:	2000 to the present
Series:	Jungle Book

Doulton Number	Price U.S. $	Can. $	U.K. £	Aust. $
JB1	—	—	60.00	—

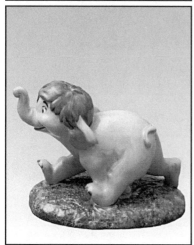

JB2
BABY ELEPHANT™

Designer:	Martyn Alcock
Modeller:	Martyn Alcock
Height:	3 ¼", 8.3 cm
Colour:	Tan
Issued:	2000 to the present
Series:	Jungle Book

Doulton Number	Price U.S. $	Can. $	U.K. £	Aust. $
JB2	—	—	45.00	—

JB3
BALOO™

Designer:	Shane Ridge
Modeller:	Shane Ridge
Height:	5 ¼", 13.3 cm
Colour:	Grey and white
Issued:	2000 to the present
Series:	Jungle Book

Doulton Number	Price U.S. $	Can. $	U.K. £	Aust. $
JB3	—	—	70.00	—

JB4
BAGHEERA™

Designer:	Shane Ridge
Modeller:	Shane Ridge
Height:	4 ¾", 12.1 cm
Colour:	Black
Issued:	2000 to the present
Series:	Jungle Book

Doulton	Price			
Number	U.S. $	Can. $	U.K. £	Aust. $
JB4	—	—	70.00	—

JB5
SHERE KHAN™

Designer:	Martyn Alcock
Modeller:	Martyn Alcock
Height:	3 ¼", 8.3 cm
Colour:	Yellow with dark brown stripes
Issued:	2000 to the present
Series:	Jungle Book

Doulton	Price			
Number	U.S. $	Can. $	U.K. £	Aust. $
JB5	—	—	85.00	—

DISNEY VILLAINS COLLECTION
1997-1998

HN 3839
CRUELLA DE VIL™
Style Two

Designer:	Pauline Parsons
Height:	8", 20.3 cm
Colour:	Black dress, white fur coat, red gloves
Issued:	1997 in a limited edition of 2,000
Series:	The Disney Villains Collection

Back Stamp	Doulton Number	Price			
		U.S. $	Can. $	U.K. £	Aust. $
Doulton	HN 3839	450.00	650.00	250.00	625.00

HN 3840
MALEFICENT™

Designer:	Pauline Parsons
Height:	8", 20.3 cm
Colour:	Black and purple
Issued:	1997 in a limited edition of 2,000
Series:	The Disney Villains Collection

Back Stamp	Doulton Number	Price			
		U.S. $	Can. $	U.K. £	Aust. $
Doulton	HN 3840	450.00	650.00	250.00	625.00

HN 3847
THE QUEEN™

Designer:	Pauline Parson
Height:	8 ¾", 22.2 cm
Colour:	Black, white, purple, red and yellow
Issued:	1998 in a limited edition of 2,000
Series:	The Disney Villains Collection

Back Stamp	Doulton Number	Price			
		U.S. $	Can. $	U.K. £	Aust. $
Doulton	HN 3847	350.00	500.00	175.00	500.00

HN 3848
THE WITCH™

Designer:	Pauline Parsons
Height:	7", 17.8 cm
Colour:	Black robes, red apple
Issued:	1998 in a limited edition of 2,000
Series:	The Disney Villains Collection

Back Stamp	Doulton Number	Price			
		U.S. $	Can. $	U.K. £	Aust. $
Doulton	HN 3848	350.00	500.00	175.00	500.00

FANTASIA 2000

FAN1
BUCKETS OF MISCHIEF™

Designer:	Shane Ridge
Modeller:	Shane Ridge
Height:	4 ½", 11.9 cm
Colour:	Brown broom and buckets, blue water
Issued:	2000 in a limited edition of 2,000
Series:	Fantasia 2000

Back Stamp	Doulton Number	Price			
		U.S. $	Can. $	U.K. £	Aust. $
FAN1	8226	—	—	60.00	—

FAN2
FOLLOW ME™

Designer:	Shane Ridge
Modeller:	Shane Ridge
Height:	5 ¼", 13.3 cm
Colour:	Red, purple, black and white
Issued:	2000 in a limited edition of 2,000
Series:	Fantasia 2000

Back Stamp	Doulton Number	Price			
		U.S. $	Can. $	U.K. £	Aust. $
FAN2	8227	—	—	80.00	—

FAN3
NOAH'S™ HELPER

Designer:	Shane Ridge
Modeller:	Shane Ridge
Height:	4", 10.1 cm
Colour:	Brown, white and yellow
Issued:	2000 in a limited edition of 2,000
Series:	Fantasia 2000

Back Stamp	Doulton Number	Price			
		U.S. $	Can. $	U.K. £	Aust. $
FAN3	8228	—	—	75.00	—

FAN4
HEART ON A STRING™

Designer:	Shane Ridge
Modeller:	Shane Ridge
Height:	4 ¼", 10.8 cm
Colour:	Blue, yellow and white
Issued:	2000 in a limited edition of 2,000
Series:	Fantasia 2000

Back Stamp	Doulton Number	U.S. $	Can. $	U.K. £	Aust. $
				Price	
FAN4	8325	—	—	80.00	—

FAN5
A FLOWER AND HIS HEART™

Designer:	Shane Ridge
Modeller:	Shane Ridge
Height:	6 ½", 16.5 cm
Colour:	Red, white and pink
Issued:	2000 in a limited edition of 2,000
Series:	1. Fantasia 2000
	2. Tableau

Back Stamp	Doulton Number	U.S. $	Can. $	U.K. £	Aust. $
				Price	
FAN5	8225	—	—	215.00	—

FILM CLASSICS COLLECTION

CN1
CINDERELLA™ THE DRESS OF THE DREAMS

Designer:	Shane Ridge
Modeller:	Shane Ridge
Height:	6 ¾", 17.2 cm
Colour:	Pink and white dress
Issued:	2000 in a limited edition of 2,000
Series:	Film Classics Collection

Back Stamp	Doulton Number	Price			
		U.S. $	Can. $	U.K. £	Aust. $
CN1	—	—	—	120.00	—

FC1
BAMBI™

Designer:	Martyn Alcock
Modeller:	Martyn Alcock
Height:	4", 10.1 cm
Colour:	Brown deer, yellow spots, black nose and tip on top of ears
Issued:	1999 in a limited edition of 1,500
Series:	Film Classics Collection

Back Stamp	Doulton Number	Price			
		U.S. $	Can. $	U.K. £	Aust. $
FC1	4440	—	—	70.00	—

FC2
THUMPER™
Style Two

Designer:	Martyn Alcock
Modeller:	Martyn Alcock
Height:	3 ¼", 8.3 cm
Colour:	Grey, white and cream rabbit, pink nose
Issued:	1999 in a limited edition on 1,500
Series:	Film Classics Collection

Back Stamp	Doulton Number	Price			
		U.S. $	Can. $	U.K. £	Aust. $
FC2	4432	—	—	60.00	—

FC3
DUMBO™

Modeller:	Shane Ridge
Height:	4 ½", 11.9 cm
Colour:	Grey elephant, pink inner ears
Issued:	1999 in a limited edition of 1,500
Series:	Film Classics Collection

Back Stamp	Doulton Number	U.S. $	Can. $	Price U.K. £	Aust. $
FC3	4427	—	—	95.00	—

FC4
PINOCCHIO™
Style Two

Designer:	Shane Ridge
Modeller:	Shane Ridge
Height:	5 ½", 14.0 cm
Colour:	Yellow shirt and hat, red trousers and shoes, blue neck tie and book
Issued:	1999 in a limited edition of 1,500
Series:	Film Classics Collection

Back Stamp	Doulton Number	U.S. $	Can. $	Price U.K. £	Aust. $
FC4	4431	—	—	95.00	—

FC5
JIMINY CRICKET™
Style Two

Designer:	Warren Platt
Modeller:	Warren Platt
Height:	4 ¼", 10.8 cm
Colour:	Dark blue jacket and shoes, tan trousers, orange vest, blue hat with orange band, red umbrella
Issued:	2000 in a limited edition of 1,500
Series:	Film Classics Collection

Back Stamp	Doulton Number	Price			
		U.S. $	Can. $	U.K. £	Aust. $
FC5	3149	—	—	75.00	—

FC6
TIMOTHY MOUSE™

Designer:	Amanda Hughes-Lubeck
Modeller:	Amanda Hughes-Lubeck
Height:	3 ¼", 8.3 cm
Colour:	Red and yellow suit and hat
Issued:	2000 in a limited edition of 1,500
Series:	Film Classics Collection

Back Stamp	Doulton Number	Price			
		U.S. $	Can. $	U.K. £	Aust. $
FC6	—	—	—	65.00	—

MICKEY MOUSE COLLECTION

1998-2000

MM1/MM7
MICKEY MOUSE™
Style Two

Designer:	Warren Platt
Modeller:	Warren Platt
Height:	4 ¾", 12.1 cm
Colour:	Black, red and light brown
Issued:	1. 1998 - 1998
	2. 1999 - 2000
Series:	Mickey Mouse Collection

Back Stamp	Doulton Number	Price			
		U.S. $	Can. $	U.K. £	Aust. $
BK-1 / 70th Anniv.	MM1	100.00	150.00	60.00	150.00
BK-2	MM7	100.00	150.00	60.00	150.00

MM2/MM8
MINNIE MOUSE™
Style Two

Designer:	Warren Platt
Modeller:	Warren Platt
Height:	5 ½", 14.0 cm
Colour:	Black, blue and red
Issued:	1. 1998 - 1998
	2. 1999 - 2000
Series:	Mickey Mouse Collection

Back Stamp	Doulton Number	Price			
		U.S. $	Can. $	U.K. £	Aust. $
BK-1 / 70th Anniv.	MM2	100.00	150.00	60.00	150.00
BK-2	MM8	100.00	150.00	60.00	150.00

MM3/MM9
DONALD DUCK™
Style Two

Designer:	Warren Platt
Modeller:	Shane Ridge
Height:	4 ¾", 12.1 cm
Colour:	Blue, white and red
Issued:	1. 1998 - 1998
	2. 1999 - 2000
Series:	Mickey Mouse Collection

Back Stamp	Doulton Number	Price			
		U.S. $	Can. $	U.K. £	Aust. $
BK-1 / 70 Anniv.	MM3	100.00	150.00	60.00	150.00
BK-2	MM9	100.00	150.00	60.00	150.00

MM4/MM10
DAISY DUCK™

Designer:	Shane Ridge
Modeller:	Shane Ridge
Height:	5 ½", 14.0 cm
Colour:	Blue, white and pink
Issued:	1. 1998 - 1998
	2. 1999 - 2000
Series:	Mickey Mouse Collection

Back Stamp	Doulton Number	Price			
		U.S. $	Can. $	U.K. £	Aust. $
BK-1 / 70th Anniv.	MM4	100.00	150.00	60.00	150.00
BK-2	MM10	100.00	150.00	60.00	150.00

MM5/MM11
GOOFY™
Style Two

Designer:	Shane Ridge
Modeller:	Graham Tongue
Height:	5", 12.7 cm
Colour:	Red, blue and black
Issued:	1. 1998 - 1998
	2. 1999 - 2000
Series:	Mickey Mouse Collection

Back Stamp	Doulton Number	Price			
		U.S. $	Can. $	U.K. £	Aust. $
BK-1 / 70th Anniv.	MM5	100.00	150.00	60.00	150.00
BK-2	MM11	100.00	150.00	60.00	150.00

MM6/MM12
PLUTO™
Style Two

Designer:	Graham Tongue
Modeller:	Graham Tongue
Height:	4 ½", 12.1 cm
Colour:	Light brown
Issued:	1. 1998 - 1998
	2. 1999 - 2000
Series:	Mickey Mouse Collection

Back Stamp	Doulton Number	Price			
		U.S. $	Can. $	U.K. £	Aust. $
BK-1 / 70th Anniv.	MM6	100.00	150.00	60.00	150.00
BK-2	MM12	100.00	150.00	60.00	150.00

PETER PAN

1953-1965

1301
NANA™

Designer:	Jan Granoska
Height:	3 ¼", 8.3 cm
Colour:	Brown dog, white frilled cap with blue ribbon
Issued:	1953 - 1965
Series:	Peter Pan

Back Stamp	Beswick Number	Price			
		U.S. $	Can. $	U.K. £	Aust. $
Beswick Gold	1301	750.00	1,000.00	450.00	1,000.00

1302
SMEE™

Designer:	Jan Granoska
Height:	4 ¼", 10.8 cm
Colour:	Blue and white shirt, blue pants, red cap, green bottle
Issued:	1953 - 1965
Series:	Peter Pan

Smee
COPYRIGHT
WALT DISNEY LTD
BESWICK
ENGLAND

Back Stamp	Beswick Number	Price			
		U.S. $	Can. $	U.K. £	Aust. $
Beswick Gold	1302	700.00	900.00	400.00	950.00

1307
PETER PAN™

Designer:	Jan Granoska
Height:	5", 12.7 cm
Colour:	Light green tunic, dark green pants, brown shoes, red and green cap
Issued:	1953 - 1965
Series:	Peter Pan

Back Stamp	Beswick Number	Price			
		U.S. $	Can. $	U.K. £	Aust. $
Beswick Gold	1307	1,000.00	1,300.00	600.00	1,350.00

1312
TINKER BELL™

Designer:	Jan Granoska
Height:	5", 12.7 cm
Colour:	Light green dress, dark green wings and shoes
Issued:	1953 - 1965
Series:	Peter Pan

Back Stamp	Beswick Number	Price			
		U.S. $	Can. $	U.K. £	Aust. $
Beswick Gold	1312	900.00	1,200.00	550.00	1,200.00

SNOW WHITE AND THE SEVEN DWARFS

BESWICK SERIES 1954-1967

1325
DOPEY™
Style One

Designer: Arthur Gredington
Height: 3 ½", 8.9 cm
Colour: Green coat, maroon cap, grey shoes
Issued: 1954 - 1967
Series: Snow White and the Seven Dwarfs (Series One)

Back Stamp	Beswick Number	Price			
		U.S. $	Can. $	U.K. £	Aust. $
Beswick Gold	1325	425.00	550.00	185.00	400.00

1326
HAPPY™
Style One

Designer: Arthur Gredington
Height: 3 ½", 8.9 cm
Colour: Purple tunic, light blue trousers, light brown cap, brown shoes
Issued: 1954 - 1967
Series: Snow White and the Seven Dwarfs (Series One)

Back Stamp	Beswick Number	Price			
		U.S. $	Can. $	U.K. £	Aust. $
Beswick Gold	1326	425.00	550.00	185.00	400.00

1327
BASHFUL™
Style One

Designer: Arthur Gredington
Height: 3 ½", 8.9 cm
Colour: Brown tunic, purple trousers, grey cap, brown shoes
Issued: 1954 - 1967
Series: Snow White and the Seven Dwarfs (Series One)

Back Stamp	Beswick Number	Price			
		U.S. $	Can. $	U.K. £	Aust. $
Beswick Gold	1327	425.00	550.00	185.00	400.00

1328
SNEEZY™
Style One

Designer:	Arthur Gredington
Height:	3 ½", 8.9 cm
Colour:	Green tunic, purple trousers, brown cap and shoes
Issued:	1954 - 1967
Series:	Snow White and the Seven Dwarfs (Series One)

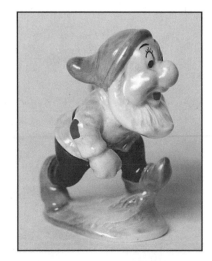

Back Stamp	Beswick Number	U.S. $	Can. $	U.K. £	Aust. $
Beswick Gold	1328	425.00	550.00	185.00	400.00

1329
DOC™
Style One

Designer:	Arthur Gredington
Height:	3 ½", 8.9 cm
Colour:	Brown tunic, blue trousers, yellow cap, brown shoes
Issued:	1954 - 1967
Series:	Snow White and the Seven Dwarfs (Series One)

Back Stamp	Beswick Number	U.S. $	Can. $	U.K. £	Aust. $
Beswick Gold	1329	425.00	550.00	200.00	400.00

1330
GRUMPY™
Style One

Designer:	Arthur Gredington
Height:	3 ¾", 9.5 cm
Colour:	Purple tunic, red trousers, blue cap, brown shoes
Issued:	1954 - 1967
Series:	Snow White and the Seven Dwarfs (Series One)

Back Stamp	Beswick Number	U.S. $	Can. $	U.K. £	Aust. $
Beswick Gold	1330	425.00	550.00	185.00	400.00

1331
SLEEPY™
Style One

Designer:	Arthur Gredington
Height:	3 ½", 8.9 cm
Colour:	Tan tunic, red trousers, green hat, grey shoes
Issued:	1954 - 1967
Series:	Snow White and the Seven Dwarfs (Series One)

Back Stamp	Beswick Number	Price			
		U.S. $	Can. $	U.K. £	Aust. $
Beswick Gold	1331	425.00	550.00	185.00	400.00

1332A
SNOW WHITE™
Style One
First Version (Hair in Flounces)

Designer:	Arthur Gredington
Height:	5 ½", 14.0 cm
Colour:	Yellow and purple dress, red cape, white collar
Issued:	1954 - 1955

Back Stamp	Beswick Number	Price			
		U.S. $	Can. $	U.K. £	Aust. $
Beswick Gold	1332A		Extremely rare		

Note: Snow White (Style One) was remodelled February 1955.

1332B
SNOW WHITE™
Style One
Second Version (Hair Flat to Head)

Designer:	Arthur Gredington
Height:	5 ½", 14.0 cm
Colour:	Yellow and purple dress, red cape, white collar
Issued:	1955 - 1967
Series:	Snow White and the Seven Dwarfs (Series One)

Back Stamp	Beswick Number	Price			
		U.S. $	Can. $	U.K. £	Aust. $
Beswick Gold	1332B	800.00	975.00	425.00	750.00

SNOW WHITE AND THE SEVEN DWARFS
ROYAL DOULTON SERIES 1997 to the present

SW1 / SW9
SNOW WHITE™
Style Three

Designer:	Amanda Hughes-Lubeck
Height:	5 ¾", 14.6 cm
Colour:	Yellow and blue dress, red cape, white collar
Issued:	SW1 1997 in a limited edition of 2,000 SW9 1998 to the present
Series:	Snow White and the Seven Dwarfs (Series Two)

Back Stamp	Beswick Number	Price			
		U.S. $	Can. $	U.K. £	Aust. $
Doulton/Disney 60th	SW 1	300.00	400.00	150.00	425.00
Doulton/Disney	SW 9	—	—	87.00	—

SW2 / SW10
DOC™
Style Two

Designer:	Amanda Hughes-Lubeck
Height:	3 ¼", 8.3 cm
Colour:	Red jacket, brown trousers, yellow hat, green book
Issued:	SW2 1997 in a limited edition of 2,000 SW10 1998 - 1999
Series:	Snow White and the Seven Dwarfs (Series Two)

Back Stamp	Beswick Number	Price			
		U.S. $	Can. $	U.K. £	Aust. $
Doulton/Disney 60th	SW 2	100.00	150.00	50.00	165.00
Doulton/Disney	SW 10	40.00	60.00	25.00	60.00

SW3 / SW11
GRUMPY™
Style Two

Designer:	Shane Ridge
Height:	3 ½", 8.9 cm
Colour:	Dark rust coat and trousers, brown hat, light brown basket
Issued:	SW3 1997 in a limited edition of 2,000 SW11 1998 to the present
Series:	Snow White and the Seven Dwarfs (Series Two)

Back Stamp	Beswick Number	Price			
		U.S. $	Can. $	U.K. £	Aust. $
Doulton/Disney 60th	SW 3	100.00	150.00	50.00	165.00
Doulton/Disney	SW 11	—	—	25.50	

SW4 / SW12
HAPPY™
Style Two

Designer:	Amanda Hughes-Lubeck
Height:	3 ½", 8.9 cm
Colour:	Brown vest, orange shirt, light blue trousers with black belt and a yellow hat
Issued:	SW4 1997 in a limited edition of 2,000
	SW12 1998 to the present
Series:	Snow White and the Seven Dwarfs (Series Two)

Back Stamp	Beswick Number	Price			
		U.S. $	Can. $	U.K. £	Aust. $
Doulton/Disney 60th	SW 4	100.00	150.00	50.00	165.00
Doulton/Disney	SW 12	—	—	25.00	—

SW5 / SW13
DOPEY™
Style Two

Designer:	Shane Ridge
Height:	3 ½", 8.9 cm
Colour:	Yellow shirt and trousers, purple hat, black belt
Issued:	SW5 1997 in a limited edition of 2,000
	SW13 1998 - 2000
Series:	Snow White and the Seven Dwarfs (Series Two)

Back Stamp	Beswick Number	Price			
		U.S. $	Can. $	U.K. £	Aust. $
Doulton/Disney 60th	SW 5	100.00	150.00	50.00	165.00
Doulton/Disney	SW 13	40.00	60.00	25.00	60.00

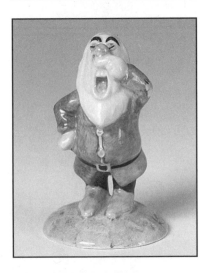

SW6 / SW14
SNEEZY™
Style Two

Designer:	Warren Platt
Height:	3 ½", 8.9 cm
Colour:	Light brown jacket, dark brown trousers, black belt
Issued:	SW6 1997 in a limited edition of 2,000
	SW14 1998 to the present
Series:	Snow White and the Seven Dwarfs (Series Two)

Back Stamp	Beswick Number	Price			
		U.S. $	Can. $	U.K. £	Aust. $
Doulton/Disney 60th	SW 6	100.00	150.00	50.00	165.00
Doulton/Disney	SW 14	—	—	25.00	—

SW7 / SW15
SLEEPY™
Style Two

Designer:	Warren Platt
Height:	3 ½", 8.9 cm
Colour:	Beige jacket, dark brown trousers, green hat and a yellow bottle
Issued:	SW7 1997 in a limited edition of 2,000
	SW15 1998 to the present
Series:	Snow White and the Seven Dwarfs (Series Two)

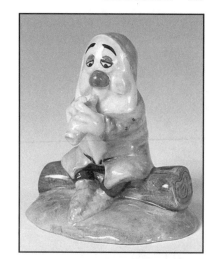

Back Stamp	Beswick Number	Price U.S. $	Can. $	U.K. £	Aust. $
Doulton/Disney 60th	SW 7	100.00	150.00	50.00	165.00
Doulton/Disney	SW 15	—	—	25.00	

SW8 / SW16
BASHFUL™
Style Two

Designer:	Amanda Hughes-Lubeck
Height:	3 ½", 8.9 cm
Colour:	Dark yellow jacket, light brown trousers, green hat
Issued:	SW8 1997 in a limited edition of 2,000
	SW16 1998 - 1999
Series:	Snow White and the Seven Dwarfs (Series Two)

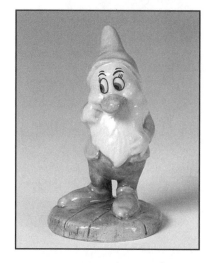

Back Stamp	Beswick Number	Price U.S. $	Can. $	U.K. £	Aust. $
Doulton/Disney 60th	SW 8	100.00	150.00	50.00	165.00
Doulton/Disney	SW 16	40.00	60.00	25.00	60.00

SW17
DOPEY™ BY CANDLELIGHT

Designer:	Shane Ridge
Height:	3 ½", 8.9 cm
Colour:	Green
Issued:	1998 to the present
Series:	Snow White and the Seven Dwarfs

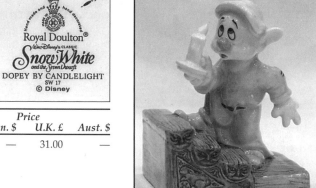

Back Stamp	Beswick Number	Price U.S. $	Can. $	U.K. £	Aust. $
Doulton/Disney	SW 17	—	—	31.00	—

SW18
BASHFUL'S™ MELODY

Designer:	Graham Tongue
Modeller:	Graham Tongue
Height:	3 ½", 8.9 cm
Colour:	Blue
Issued:	1998 to the present
Series:	Snow White and the Seven Dwarfs

Back Stamp	Beswick Number	Price U.S. $	Can. $	U.K. £	Aust. $
Doulton/Disney	SW 18	—	—	27.00	—

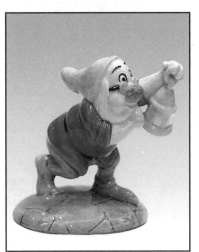

SW19
DOC™ WITH LANTERN

Designer:	Warren Platt
Modeller:	Warren Platt
Height:	3 ½", 8.9 cm
Colour:	Red and yellow
Issued:	1999 to the present
Series:	Snow White and the Seven Dwarfs

Back Stamp	Beswick Number	Price U.S. $	Can. $	U.K. £	Aust. $
Doulton/Disney	SW 19	—	—	26.00	—

SW20
GRUMPY'S™ BATHTIME

Designer:	Shane Ridge
Modeller:	Shane Ridge
Height:	3 ½", 8.9 cm
Colour:	White, brown, red and yellow
Issued:	1999 - 1999
Series:	Snow White and the Seven Dwarfs

Back Stamp	Beswick Number	Price U.S. $	Can. $	U.K. £	Aust. $
Doulton/Disney	SW 20	55.00	80.00	35.00	80.00

Note: Serial numbered

SW21
DOPEY'S™ FIRST KISS

Designer:	Walt Disney
Modeller:	Shane Ridge
Height:	5 ¼", 13.3 cm
Colour:	Yellow, blue, red and green
Issued:	2000 in a limited edition of 2,000
Series:	1. Disney Classics
	2. Tableau

Back Stamp	Beswick Number	Price U.S. $	Can. $	U.K. £	Aust. $
Doulton/Disney	SW 21	—	—	150.00	—

WINNIE THE POOH

BESWICK SERIES 1968-1990

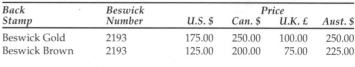

2193
WINNIE THE POOH™

Designer:	Albert Hallam
Height:	2 ½", 6.4 cm
Colour:	Golden brown and red
Issued:	1968 - 1990
Series:	Winnie The Pooh

Back Stamp	Beswick Number	Price U.S. $	Can. $	U.K. £	Aust. $
Beswick Gold	2193	175.00	250.00	100.00	250.00
Beswick Brown	2193	125.00	200.00	75.00	225.00

2196
EEYORE™

Designer:	Albert Hallam
Height:	2", 5.0 cm
Colour:	Grey with black markings
Issued:	1968 - 1990
Series:	Winnie The Pooh

Back Stamp	Beswick Number	Price U.S. $	Can. $	U.K. £	Aust. $
Beswick Gold	2196	175.00	250.00	100.00	250.00
Beswick Brown	2196	125.00	200.00	80.00	225.00

2214
PIGLET™

Designer:	Albert Hallam
Height:	2 ¾", 7.0 cm
Colour:	Pink and red
Issued:	1968 - 1990
Series:	Winnie The Pooh

Back Stamp	Beswick Number	Price U.S. $	Can. $	U.K. £	Aust. $
Beswick Gold	2214	175.00	250.00	100.00	250.00
Beswick Brown	2214	125.00	200.00	85.00	225.00

2215
RABBIT™

Designer:	Albert Hallam
Height:	3 ¼", 8.3 cm
Colour:	Brown and beige
Issued:	1968 - 1990
Series:	Winnie The Pooh

Back Stamp	Beswick Number	Price			
		U.S. $	Can. $	U.K. £	Aust. $
Beswick Gold	2215	225.00	300.00	125.00	300.00
Beswick Brown	2215	175.00	200.00	85.00	250.00

2216
OWL™

Designer:	Albert Hallam
Height:	3", 7.6 cm
Colour:	Brown, white and black
Issued:	1968 - 1990
Series:	Winnie The Pooh

Back Stamp	Beswick Number	Price			
		U.S. $	Can. $	U.K. £	Aust. $
Beswick Gold	2216	175.00	250.00	90.00	225.00
Beswick Brown	2216	125.00	175.00	75.00	200.00

2217
KANGA™

Designer:	Albert Hallam
Height:	3 ¼", 8.3 cm
Colour:	Dark and light brown
Issued:	1968 - 1990
Series:	Winnie The Pooh

Back Stamp	Beswick Number	Price			
		U.S. $	Can. $	U.K. £	Aust. $
Beswick Gold	2217	200.00	300.00	110.00	275.00
Beswick Brown	2217	150.00	200.00	75.00	225.00

2394
TIGGER™

Designer:	Graham Tongue
Height:	3", 7.6 cm
Colour:	Yellow with black stripes
Issued:	1971 - 1990
Series:	Winnie The Pooh

Back Stamp	Beswick Number	Price U.S. $	Can. $	U.K. £	Aust. $
Beswick Gold	2394	300.00	400.00	200.00	375.00
Beswick Brown	2394	225.00	300.00	135.00	325.00

2395
CHRISTOPHER ROBIN™
Style One

Designer:	Graham Tongue
Height:	4 ¾", 12.1 cm
Colour:	Yellow, blue and white
Issued:	1971 - 1990
Series:	Winnie The Pooh

Back Stamp	Beswick Number	Price U.S. $	Can. $	U.K. £	Aust. $
Beswick Gold	2395	350.00	475.00	200.00	450.00
Beswick Brown	2395	300.00	400.00	165.00	400.00

WINNIE THE POOH
ROYAL DOULTON SERIES 1996 to the present

WP 1
WINNIE THE POOH™ AND THE HONEY POT

Designer:	Warren Platt
Height:	2 ½", 6.5 cm
Colour:	Yellow bear, red jersey, red-brown honey pot
Issued:	1996 - 1999
Series:	Winnie the Pooh and Friends from the One Hundred Acre Wood

Back Stamp	Doulton Number	Price U.S. $	Can. $	U.K. £	Aust. $
BK-1	WP 1 / 70th	100.00	150.00	70.00	150.00
BK-2	WP 1	40.00	70.00	25.00	70.00

WP 2
POOH™ AND PIGLET™ THE WINDY DAY

Designer:	Martyn Alcock
Height:	3 ¼", 8.3 cm
Colour:	Yellow bear, pink piglet with green suit, light brown base
Issued:	1996 to the present
Series:	Winnie the Pooh and Friends from the One Hundred Acre Wood

Back Stamp	Doulton Number	Price U.S. $	Can. $	U.K. £	Aust. $
BK-1	WP 2 / 70th	85.00	125.00	50.00	125.00
BK-2	WP 2	50.00	—	30.00	—

WP 3
WINNIE THE POOH™ AND THE PAW-MARKS™

Designer:	Warren Platt
Height:	2 ¾", 7.0 cm
Colour:	Yellow bear, red jersey
Issued:	1996 - 1997
Series:	Winnie the Pooh and Friends from the One Hundred Acre Wood

Back Stamp	Doulton Number	Price U.S. $	Can. $	U.K. £	Aust. $
BK-1	WP 3 / 70th	85.00	125.00	50.00	125.00
BK-2	WP 3	50.00	75.00	35.00	75.00

WP 4
WINNIE THE POOH™ IN THE ARMCHAIR

Designer: Shane Ridge
Height: 3 ¼", 8.3 cm
Colour: Yellow bear, pink armchair
Issued: 1996 - 1998
Series: Winnie the Pooh and Friends
           from the One Hundred Acre Wood

Back Stamp	Doulton Number	Price			
		U.S. $	Can. $	U.K. £	Aust. $
BK-1	WP 4 / 70th	85.00	125.00	50.00	125.00
BK-2	WP 4	35.00	70.00	25.00	75.00

WP 5
PIGLET™ AND THE BALLOON

Designer: Warren Platt
Height: 2 ¾", 7.0 cm
Colour: Pink piglet, green suit, blue
           balloon, light brown base
Issued: 1996 - 1998
Series: Winnie the Pooh and Friends
           from the One Hundred Acre Wood

Back Stamp	Doulton Number	Price			
		U.S. $	Can. $	U.K. £	Aust. $
BK-1	WP 5 / 70th	75.00	110.00	45.00	110.00
BK-2	WP 5	40.00	65.00	25.00	65.00

WP 6
TIGGER™ SIGNS THE RISSOLUTION

Designer: Martyn Alcock
Height: 1 ¾", 4.5 cm
Colour: Yellow and black
Issued: 1996 to the present
Series: Winnie the Pooh and Friends
           from the One Hundred Acre Wood

Back Stamp	Doulton Number	Price			
		U.S. $	Can. $	U.K. £	Aust. $
BK-1	WP 6 / 70th	75.00	110.00	45.00	110.00
BK-2	WP 6	35.00	—	22.00	—

WP 7
EEYORE'S™ TAIL

Designer:	Shane Ridge
Height:	3 ½", 8.9 cm
Colour:	Grey donkey with black markings, pink bow
Issued:	1996 - 1999
Series:	Winnie the Pooh and Friends from the One Hundred Acre Wood

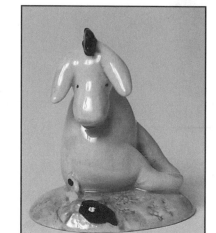

Back Stamp	Doulton Number	Price			
		U.S. $	Can. $	U.K. £	Aust. $
BK-1	WP 7 / 70th	75.00	110.00	45.00	110.00
BK-2	WP 7	35.00	70.00	25.00	70.00

WP 8
KANGA™ AND ROO™

Designer:	Martyn Alcock
Height:	3 ½", 8.9 cm
Colour:	Dark and light brown kangaroos
Issued:	1996 - 1998
Series:	Winnie the Pooh and Friends from the One Hundred Acre Wood

Back Stamp	Doulton Number	Price			
		U.S. $	Can. $	U.K. £	Aust. $
BK-1	WP 8 / 70th	75.00	110.00	50.00	110.00
BK-2	WP 8	45.00	70.00	25.00	70.00

WP 9
CHRISTOPHER ROBIN™
Style Two

Designer:	Shane Ridge
Height:	5 ½", 14.0 cm
Colour:	White and blue checkered shirt, blue shorts, black wellingtons, red-brown hair
Issued:	1996 to the present
Series:	Winnie the Pooh and Friends from the One Hundred Acre Wood

Back Stamp	Doulton Number	Price			
		U.S. $	Can. $	U.K. £	Aust. $
BK-1	WP 9 / 70th	100.00	150.00	60.00	150.00
BK-2	WP 9	45.00	—	26.00	—

WP 10
CHRISTOPHER ROBIN™ AND POOH™

Designer:	Shane Ridge
Height:	3 ¼", 8.5 cm
Colour:	Light blue shirt and shorts, black boots, reddish brown hair, yellow bear
Issued:	1996 - 1997
Series:	Winnie the Pooh and Friends from the One Hundred Acre Wood

Back Stamp	Doulton Number	Price			
		U.S. $	Can. $	U.K. £	Aust. $
BK-1	WP 10 / 70th	150.00	225.00	90.00	225.00
BK-2	WP 10	85.00	125.00	55.00	125.00

WP 11
POOH™ LIGHTS THE CANDLE

Designer:	Graham Tongue
Height:	3 ½", 8.9 cm
Colour:	Yellow bear with white candle and hat
Issued:	1997 - 1998
Series:	Winnie the Pooh and Friends from the One Hundred Acre Wood

Back Stamp	Doulton Number	Price			
		U.S. $	Can. $	U.K. £	Aust. $
BK-2	WP 11	45.00	70.00	25.00	80.00

WP 12
POOH™ COUNTING THE HONEYPOTS

Designer:	Martyn Alcock
Height:	3 ½", 8.9 cm
Colour:	Yellow bear, brown honeypots
Issued:	1997 - 1999
Series:	Winnie the Pooh and Friends from the One Hundred Acre Wood

Back Stamp	Doulton Number	Price			
		U.S. $	Can. $	U.K. £	Aust. $
BK-2	WP 12	35.00	70.00	25.00	80.00

WP 13
PIGLET™ PICKING THE VIOLETS

Designer: Graham Tongue
Height: 2 ½", 6.4 cm
Colour: Pink, light and dark greens
Issued: 1997 to the present
Series: Winnie the Pooh and Friends
               from the One Hundred Acre Wood

Back Stamp	Doulton Number	Price			
		U.S. $	Can. $	U.K. £	Aust. $
BK-2	WP 13	35.00	—	22.00	—

WP 14
EEYORE'S™ BIRTHDAY

Designer: Martyn Alcock
Height: 2 ¾", 7.0 cm
Colour: Grey and black
Issued: 1997 to the present
Series: Winnie the Pooh and Friends
               from the One Hundred Acre Wood

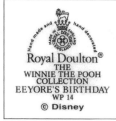

Back Stamp	Doulton Number	Price			
		U.S. $	Can. $	U.K. £	Aust. $
BK-2	WP 14	35.00	—	23.00	—

WP 15
EEYORE™ LOSES A TAIL

Designer: Martyn Alcock
Height: 4", 10.1 cm
Colour: Pink, yellow, grey,
               green and brown
Issued: 1997 in a limited edition
               of 5,000
Series: 1. Tableau
               2. Winnie the Pooh and Friends
                  from the One Hundred Acre Wood

Back Stamp	Doulton Number	Price			
		U.S. $	Can. $	U.K. £	Aust. $
Doulton	WP 15	300.00	450.00	175.00	475.00

WP 16
POOH'S™ BLUE BALLOON
MONEY BOX

Designer: Shane Ridge
Height: 4 ¼", 10.8 cm
Colour: Yellow bear, pink pig
        wearing green jumper,
        white balloon with dark
        blue rope
Issued: 1997 - 1998
Series: Winnie the Pooh and
        Friends from the One
        Hundred Acre Wood

Back Stamp	Doulton Number	Price			
		U.S. $	Can. $	U.K. £	Aust. $
Doulton	WP16	60.00	85.00	35.00	85.00

WP 17
WOL™ SIGNS THE RISSOLUTION

Designer: Martyn Alcock
Height: 3 ¾", 9.5 cm
Colour: Grey and black
Issued: 1998 in a special edition of 2,500
Series: Winnie the Pooh and Friends
        from the One Hundred Acre Wood

Back Stamp	Doulton Number	Price			
		U.S. $	Can. $	U.K. £	Aust. $
Doulton	WP 17	225.00	300.00	140.00	300.00

WP 18
WINNIE THE POOH™ AND THE PRESENT

Designer: Graham Tongue
Height: 3 ¾", 9.5 cm
Colour: Yellow and brown
Issued: 1999 to the present
Series: Winnie the Pooh and Friends
        from the One Hundred Acre Wood

Back Stamp	Doulton Number	Price			
		U.S. $	Can. $	U.K. £	Aust. $
Doulton	WP 18	35.00	—	22.00	—

WP 19
WINNIE THE POOH™ AND THE FAIR-SIZED BASKET

Designer:	Graham Tongue
Height:	2 ¾", 7.0 cm
Colour:	Yellow and brown
Issued:	1999 to the present
Series:	Winnie the Pooh and Friends from the One Hundred Acre Wood

Back Stamp	Doulton Number	Price			
		U.S. $	Can. $	U.K. £	Aust. $
Doulton	WP 19	50.00	—	22.00	—

WP 20
THE MORE IT SNOWS, TIDDELY POM™

Designer:	Shane Ridge
Height:	3 ¼", 8.3 cm
Colour:	Yellow and red
Issued:	1999 to the present
Series:	Winnie the Pooh and Friends from the One Hundred Acre Wood

Back Stamp	Doulton Number	Price			
		U.S. $	Can. $	U.K. £	Aust. $
Doulton	WP 20	50.00	—	30.00	—

WP 21
SUMMER'S DAY PICNIC™

Designer:	Warren Platt
Length:	2 ½", 5.7 cm
Colour:	Blue , yellow and green
Issued:	1998 in a limited edition of 5,000
Series:	1. Tableau
	2. Winnie the Pooh and Friends from the One Hundred Acre Wood

Back Stamp	Doulton Number	Price			
		U.S. $	Can. $	U.K. £	Aust. $
Doulton	WP 21	250.00	375.00	125.00	350.00

WP 22
I'VE FOUND SOMEBODY JUST LIKE ME™

Designer:	Martyn Alcock
Length:	5 ¼", 13.3 cm
Colour:	Yellow, black, blue and white
Issued:	1999 in a limited edition of 5,000
Series:	1. Tableau
	2. Winnie the Pooh and Friends from the One Hundred Acre Wood

Back Stamp	Doulton Number	Price			
		U.S. $	Can. $	U.K. £	Aust. $
Doulton WP 22		200.00	250.00	125.00	275.00

WP 23
RABBIT™ READS THE PLAN

Designer:	Martyn Alcock
Height:	4 ½", 11.9 cm
Colour:	Grey rabbit, pink inner ears
Issued:	1999 - 1999
Series:	Classic Pooh

Back Stamp	Doulton Number	Price			
		U.S. $	Can. $	U.K. £	Aust. $
Doulton	WP 23	50.00	95.00	30.00	95.00

WP 24
HOW SWEET TO BE A CLOUD™ (CLOCK)

Designer:	Warren Platt
Height:	4 ½", 11.9 cm
Colour:	Blue, white, yellow and red
Issued:	2000 - 2000
Series:	Classic Pooh

Back Stamp	Doulton Number	Price			
		U.S. $	Can. $	U.K. £	Aust. $
Doulton	WP 24	—	—	67.00	—

WP 25
EEYORE™ NOSE TO THE GROUND

Designer:	Martyn Alcock
Height:	3 ¾", 9.5 cm
Size:	Large
Colour:	Grey and black
Issued:	2000 in a limited edition of 2,000
Series:	Large Size

Back Stamp	Doulton Number	U.S. $	Can. $	U.K. £	Aust. $
Doulton	WP 25	—	—	80.00	—

WP 26
PIGLET™ PLANTING A HAYCORN

Designer:	Martyn Alcock
Height:	3 ¾", 9.5 cm
Size:	Large
Colour:	Pink, green and brown
Issued:	2000 in a limited edition of 2,000
Series:	Large Size

Back Stamp	Doulton Number	U.S. $	Can. $	U.K. £	Aust. $
Doulton	WP 26	—	—	55.00	—

WP 27
TIGGER™ LOVES TIGGER LILLIES

Designer:	Martyn Alcock
Height:	4 ¼", 10.8 cm
Size:	Large
Colour:	Brown, black and red
Issued:	2000 in a limited edition of 2,000
Series:	Large Size

Back Stamp	Doulton Number	U.S. $	Can. $	U.K. £	Aust. $
Doulton	WP 27	—	—	70.00	—

WP 28
POOH BEGAN TO EAT™

Designer: Shane Ridge
Height: 3 ¾", 9.5 cm
Size: Large
Colour: Yellow and green
Issued: 2000 in a limited edition of 2,000
Series: Large Size

Back Stamp	Doulton Number	Price			
		U.S. $	Can. $	U.K. £	Aust. $
Doulton	WP 28	—	—	80.00	—

WP 29
PIGLET AND THE HONEY POT™

Designer: Amanda Hughes-Lubeck
Height: 2 ½", 6.4 cm
Colour: Green, grey and yellow
Issued: 2000 to the present
Series: Classic Pooh

Back Stamp	Doulton Number	Price			
		U.S. $	Can. $	U.K. £	Aust. $
Doulton	WP 29	—	—	30.00	—

WP 30
TIGGER PLAYS BALL™

Designer: Warren Platt
Height: 3", 7.6 cm
Colour: Brown, black and yellow
Issued: 2000 to the present
Series: Classic Pooh

Back Stamp	Doulton Number	Price			
		U.S. $	Can. $	U.K. £	Aust. $
Doulton	WP 30	—	—	60.00	—

WP 31
THE BRAIN OF POOH™

Designer:	Amanda Hughes-Lubeck
Height:	4", 10.1 cm
Colour:	Black, grey, yellow and green
Issued:	2000 in a limited edition of 5,000
Series:	Classic Pooh

Back Stamp	Doulton Number	U.S. $	Can. $	U.K. £	Aust. $
Doulton	WP 31	—	—	195.00	—

WIND IN THE WILLOWS

AW1
TOAD™
Style One

Designer:	Harry Sales
Modeller:	David Lyttleton
Height:	3 ½", 8.9 cm
Colour:	Green toad, yellow waistcoat and trousers, white shirt, red bowtie
Issued:	1987 - 1989

Back Stamp	Beswick Number	Price			
		U.S. $	Can. $	U.K. £	Aust. $
AW1	2942	110.00	150.00	75.00	125.00

AW2
BADGER™
Style One

Designer:	Harry Sales
Modeller:	David Lyttleton
Height:	3", 7.6 cm
Colour:	Black and white badger, salmon dressing gown
Issued:	1987 - 1989

Back Stamp	Beswick Number	Price			
		U.S. $	Can. $	U.K. £	Aust. $
AW2	2940	90.00	125.00	60.00	125.00

AW3
RATTY™

Designer:	Harry Sales
Modeller:	David Lyttleton
Height:	3 ½", 8.9 cm
Colour:	Blue dungarees, white shirt
Issued:	1987 - 1989

Back Stamp	Beswick Number	Price			
		U.S. $	Can. $	U.K. £	Aust. $
AW3	2941	90.00	150.00	60.00	125.00

AW4
MOLE™

Designer:	Harry Sales
Modeller:	David Lyttleton
Height:	3", 7.6 cm
Colour:	Dark grey mole, brown dressing gown
Issued:	1987 - 1989

Back Stamp	Beswick Number	Price			
		U.S. $	Can. $	U.K. £	Aust. $
AW4	2939	110.00	150.00	75.00	125.00

AW5
PORTLY™
(Otter)

Designer:	Unknown
Modeller:	Alan Maslankowski
Height:	2 ¾", 7.0 cm
Colour:	Brown otter, blue dungarees, green and yellow jumper, green shoes
Issued:	1988 - 1989

Back Stamp	Beswick Number	Price			
		U.S. $	Can. $	U.K. £	Aust. $
AW5	3065	225.00	300.00	150.00	250.00

AW6
WEASEL GAMEKEEPER™

Designer:	Unknown
Modeller:	Alan Maslankowski
Height:	4", 10.1 cm
Colour:	Brown weasel, green jacket, trousers and cap, yellow waistcoat
Issued:	1988 - 1989

Back Stamp	Beswick Number	Price			
		U.S. $	Can. $	U.K. £	Aust. $
AW6	3076	225.00	300.00	150.00	250.00

WIW1
ON THE RIVER™

Designer:	Warren Platt
Modeller:	Warren Platt
Height:	3 ½" x 6 ½", 8.9 cm x 16.5 cm
Colour:	Yellow, black and blue
Issued:	2000 in a limited edition of 1,908
Series:	Tableau

Back Stamp	Beswick Number	U.S. $	Can. $	U.K. £	Aust. $
WIW1	—		—	—	125.00	—

WIW2
TOAD™
Style Two

Designer:	Warren Platt
Modeller:	Warren Platt
Height:	4 ¾", 12.1 cm
Colour:	Brown, yellow and grey
Issued:	2000 in a limited edition of 2,000

Back Stamp	Beswick Number	U.S. $	Can. $	U.K. £	Aust. $
WIW2	—		—	—	45.00	—

WIW3
BADGER™
Style Two

Designer:	Warren Platt
Modeller:	Warren Platt
Height:	5 ½", 14.0 cm
Colour:	Red, blue and white
Issued:	2000 in a limited edition of 2,000

Back Stamp	Beswick Number	U.S. $	Can. $	U.K. £	Aust. $
WIW3	—		—	—	45.00	—

INDICES

ALPHABETICAL INDEX

MODEL NUMBER INDEX

JILL BARKLEM'S BRAMBLY HEDGE

DBH1	Poppy Eyebright
DBH2	Mr. Apple
DBH3	Mrs. Apple
DBH4	Lord Woodmouse, Style One
DBH5	Lady Woodmouse, Style One
DBH6	Dusty Dogwood
DBH7	Wilfred Toadflax
DBH8	Primrose Woodmouse
DBH9	Old Mrs Eyebright
DBH10A	Mr. Toadflax, First Version
DBH10B	Mr. Toadflax, Second Version
DBH10C	Mr. Toadflax, Third Version
DBH11	Mrs. Toadflax
DBH12	Catkin
DBH13	Old Vole
DBH14	Basil
DBH15	Mrs. Crustybread
DBH16	Clover
DBH17	Teasel
DBH18	Store Stump Money Box
DBH19	Lily Weaver
DBH20	Flax Weaver
DBH21	Conker
DBH22	Primrose Entertains
DBH23	Wilfred Entertains
DBH24	Mr. Saltapple
DBH25	Mrs. Saltapple
DBH26	Dusty and Baby
DBH30	The Ice Ball
DBH31	Lord Woodmouse, Style Two
DBH32	Lady Woodmouse, Style Two
DBH33	Primrose Picking Barries
DBH34	Wilfred Carries the Picnic
DBH35	Wilfred and the Toy Chest - Money Box

THE CAT'S CHORUS

CC1	Purrfect Pitch
CC2	Calypso Kitten
CC3	One Cool Cat
CC4	Ratcatcher Bilk
CC5	Trad Jazz Tom
CC6	Catwalking Bass
CC7	Feline Flamenco
CC8	Bravura Brass
CC9	Fat Cat
CC10	Glam Guitar

COMPTON & WOODHOUSE

—	Archie
—	Benjamin
—	Bertie
—	Henry

COUNTRY COUSINS

PM2101	Sweet Suzie "Thank You"
PM2102	Peter "Once Upon A Time"
PM2103	Harry "A New Home for Fred"
PM2104	Michael "Happily Ever After"
PM2105	Bertram "Ten Out of Ten"
PM2106	Leonardo "Practice Makes Perfect"
PM2107	Lily "Flowers Picked Just For You"
PM2108	Patrick "This Way's Best"
PM2109	Jamie "Hurrying Home"
PM2111	Mum and Lizzie "Let's Get Busy"
PM2112	Molly and Timmy "Picnic Time"
PM2113	Polly and Sarah "Good News!"
PM2114	Bill and Ted "Working Together"
PM2115	Jack and Daisy "How Does Your Garden Grow?"
PM2116	Alison and Debbie "Friendship is Fun"
PM2119	Robert and Rosie "Perfect Partners"
PM2120	Sammy "Treasure Hunting"

DAVID HAND'S ANIMALAND

1148	Dinkum Platypus
1150	Zimmy Lion
1151	Felia
1152	Ginger Nutt
1153	Hazel Nutt
1154	Oscar Ostrich
1155	Dusty Mole
1156	Loopy Hare

ENGLISH COUNTRY FOLK

ECF 1	Huntsman Fox
ECF 2	Fisherman Otter
ECF 3	Gardener Rabbit, First Variation
ECF 4	Gentleman Pig, First Variation
ECF 5	Shepherd Sheepdog
ECF 6	Hiker Badger, First Variation
ECF 7	Mrs. Rabbit Baking, First Variation
ECF 8	The Lady Pig, First Variation
ECF 9	Hiker Badger, Second Variation
ECF 10	Gentleman Pig, Second Variation
ECF 11	The Lady Pig, Second Variation
ECF 12	Gardener Rabbit, Second Variation
ECF 13	Mrs. Rabbit Baking, Second Variation

ENID BLYTON'S NODDY COLLECTION

3676	Big Ears
3678	Noddy
3679	Mr. Plod
3770	Tessie Bear

EXPRESS NEWSPAPERS PLC
Rupert Bear

2694	Rupert Bear, Style One
2710	Algy Pug
2711	Pong Ping
2720	Bill Badger, Style One
2779	Rupert Bear Snowballing
—	Bill Badger, Style Two
—	Edward Trunk
—	Podgy Pig
—	Rupert Bear, Style Two
—	Rupert Bear and Algy Pug Go-Carting
—	Rupert with Satchel

FOOTBALLING FELINES

FF2	Mee-Ouch
FF3	Kitcat
FF4	Dribble
FF5	Thrown In
FF6	Referee, Red Card

HANNA-BARBERA
The Flintstones

3577	Pebbles Flintstone
3579	Bamm Bamm
3583	Wilma Flintstone
3584	Betty Rubble
3587	Barney Rubble
3588	Fred Flintstone
3590	Dino

Top Cat

3581	Top Cat
3586	Choo-Choo
3624	Fancy Fancy
3627	Benny
3671	Officer Dibble
3673	Spook
3674	Brain

HIPPOS ON HOLIDAY

HH1	Grandma
HH2	Grandpa
HH3	Ma
HH4	Pa
HH5	Harriet
HH6	Hugo

JANE HISSEY'S OLD BEAR AND FRIENDS

OB4601	Old Bear
OB4602	Time For Bed
OB4603	Bramwell Brown Had A Good Idea
OB4604	Don't Worry Rabbit
OB4605	The Long Red Scarf
OB4606	Waiting For Snow
OB4607	The Snowflake Biscuits
OB4608	Welcome Home, Old Bear
OB4609	Ruff's Prize
OB4610	Time For A Cuddle, Hug Me Tight
OB4611	Don't Forget Old Bear
OB4612	Hold on Tight
OB4613	Resting with Cat
OB4614	Looking For A Sailor
OB4615	Too Much Food
OB4616	Nest of Socks
OB4617	Snow Decorations
OB4618	Storytime
OB4619	Duck
OB4620	Up, Up and Away

JOAN WALSH ANGLUND

2272	Anglund Boy
2293	Anglund Girl with Doll
2317	Anglund Girl with Flowers

KITTY MACBRIDE

2526	A Family Mouse
2527	A Double Act
2528	The Racegoer
2529	A Good Read
2530	Lazybones
2531	A Snack
2532	Strained Relations
2533	Just Good Friends
2565	The Ring
2566	Guilty Sweethearts
2589	All I Do is Think of You

LITTLE LIKEABLES

LL1	Family Gathering (Hen and Two Chicks)
LL2	Watching the World Go By (Frog)
LL3	Hide and Sleep (Pig and Two Piglets)
LL4	My Pony (Pony)
LL5	On Top of the World (Elephant)
LL6	Treat Me Gently (Fawn
LL7	Out at Last (Duckling)
LL8	Cats Chorus (Cats)

LITTLE LOVABLES

LL1	Happy Birthday
LL2	I Love You
LL3	God Loves Me
LL4	Just For You
LL5	To Mother
LL6	Congratulations
LL7	Passed
LL8	Happy Birthday
LL9	I Love You
LL10	God Loves Me
LL11	Just For You
LL12	To Mother
LL13	Congratulations
LL14	Passed
LL15	Happy Birthday
LL16	I Love You
LL17	God Loves Me
LL18	Just For You
LL19	To Mother
LL20	Congratulations
LL21	Passed
LL22	(No Name) Also called 'Happy Birthday'
LL23	(No Name) Also called 'I Love You'
LL24	(No Name) Also called 'God Loves Me'
LL25	(No Name) Also called 'Just for You'
LL26	(No Name) Also called 'To Mother'
LL27	(No Name) Also called 'Congratulations'
LL28	(No Name) Also called 'Passed'
LL29	To Daddy
LL30	Merry Christmas
LL31	Good Luck
LL32	Get Well Soon
LL33	Please
LL34	Please
LL35	Prototype for I Love Beswick
LL36	I Love Beswick

NORMAN THELWELL

Earthenware Series 1981-1989

2704A	An Angel on Horseback, First Variation
2704B	An Angel on Horseback, Second Variation
2769A	Kick-Start, First Variation
2769B	Kick-Start, Second Variation
2789A	Pony Express, First Variation
2789B	Pony Express, Second Variation

Resin Studio Sculptures 1985-1985

SS7A	I Forgive You, First Variation
SS7B	I Forgive You, Second Variation
SS12A	Early Bath, First Variation
SS12B	Early Bath, Second Variation

NURSERY RHYMES COLLECTION

DNR1	Humpty Dumpty
DNR2	Little Miss Muffet
DNR3	Old Mother Hubard
DNR4	The Cat and the Fiddle
DNR5	Old King Cole

PADDINGTON BEAR CO. LTD.

Resin Series

PB1	Paddington at the Station, Style One
PB2	Paddington Bakes a Cake
PB3	Paddington Decorating
PB4	Paddington Surfing
PB5	Paddington Gardening
PB6	Paddington Bathtime
PB7	Paddington the Golfer
PB8	Paddington the Musician
PB9	Paddington at Christmas Time
PB10	Paddington Marmalade Sandwich
PB11	Paddington Going to Bed
PB12	Paddington the Fisherman

Ceramic Series

—	Paddington at the Station, Style Two

THE PIG PROMENADE

PP1	John the Conductor (Vietnamese Pot Bellied Pig)
PP2	Matthew the Trumpet Player (Large White Pig)
PP3	David the Flute Player (Tamworth Pig)
PP4	Andrew the Cymbal Player (Gloucester Old Spotted Pig)
PP5	Daniel the Violinist (Saddleback Pig)
PP6	Michael the Bass Drum Player (Large Black Pig)
PP7	James The Triangle Player (Tamworth Piglet)
PP8	Richard the French Horn Player
PP9	Christopher the Guitar Player
PP10	George
PP11	Thomas
PP12	Benjamin

ST. TIGGYWINKLES

TW1	Henry Hedgehog (Standing)
TW2	Harry Hedgehog (Sitting)
TW3	Fred Fox
TW4	Bob Badger
TW5	Rosie Rabbit
TW6	Sarah Squirrel
TW7	Daniel Duck
TW8	Oliver Owl
TW9	Friends
TW10	A Helping Hand
TW11	Deborah Dormouse
TW12	Monty Mole
TW13	Franchesca Fawn

THE SNOWMAN GIFT COLLECTION
Figurines

DS1	James, Style One
DS2	The Snowman, Style One
DS3	Stylish Snowman
DS4	Thank You Snowman
DS5	Snowman Magic Music Box
DS6	Cowboy Snowman
DS7	Highland Snowman
DS8	Lady Snowman
DS9	Bass Drummer Snowman
DS10	Flautist Snowman
DS11	Violinist Snowman
DS12	Pianist Snowman
DS13	Snowman's Piano
DS14	Cymbal Player Snowman
DS15	Drummer Snowman
DS16	Trumpeter Snowman
DS17	Cellist Snowman
DS18	Snowman Musical Box
DS19	Snowman Money Box
DS20	The Snowman Tobogganing
DS21	The Snowman Skiing
DS22	The Snowman Snowballing
DS23	Building the Snowman
—	James, Style Two
—	James, Style Three
—	The Snowman, Style Two
—	The Snowman, Style Three
—	Dancing in the Snow
—	Snowman and James, The Adventure Begins

Character Jug

D6972	Snowman Miniature

SPORTING CHARACTERS

SC1	Fly Fishing
SC2	Last Lion of Defence
SC3	It's a Knockout
SC4	Sloping Off
SC5	A Round with Foxy
SC6	Out for a Duck

THUNDERBIRDS

3337	Lady Penelope
3339	Brains
3344	Scott Tracy
3345	Virgil Tracy
3346	Parker
3348	The Hood

TURNER ENTERTAINMENT

3547	Droopy
3549	Jerry
3552	Tom

The Wizard of Oz

3709	Scarecrow
3731	Lion
3732	Dorothy
3738	Tinman

20TH CENTURY ADVERTISING CLASSICS

AC1	Father William
AC2	Golly
AC3	Sir Kreemy Knut
AC4	Fox's Polar Bear
AC5	Player's 'Hero' Sailor
AC6	John Ginger
AC7	The Milky Bar Kid
AC8	Guinness Toucan

WALT DISNEY CHARACTERS
101 Dalmatians

DM 1	Cruella De Vil, Style One
DM 2	Penny
DM 3	Penny and Freckles
DM 4	Rolly
DM 5	Patch, Rolly and Freckles
DM 6	Pongo
DM 7	Perdita
DM 8	Lucky
DM 9	Patch in Basket
DM 10	Lucky and Freckles on Ice
DM 11	Pups in the Chair

Disney Characters

1278	Mickey Mouse, Style One
1279	Jiminy Cricket, Style One
1280	Pluto, Style One
1281	Goofy, Style One
1282	Pinocchio, Style One
1283	Donald Duck, Style One
1289	Minnie Mouse, Style One
1291	Thumper, Style One

Disney Princess Collection

HN 3677	Cinderella
HN 3678	Snow White, Style Two
HN 3830	Belle
HN 3831	Ariel
HN 3832	Jasmine
HN 3833	Aurora

Disney Showcase Collection
The Jungle Book

JB1	Mowgli
JB2	Baby Elephant
JB3	Baloo
JB4	Bagheera
JB5	Shere Khan

Doulton & Beswick Wares

Phillips holds a spring and autumn Doulton & Beswick wares
sale each year in London, England, which includes storybook figurines.
For expert, friendly advice on buying and selling at auction through
Phillips or for our sale catalogues, please contact Mark Oliver
on +44 (0) 20 7468 8233, moliver@philmail.demon.co.uk.

101 New Bond Street, London W1S 1SR
Telephone +44 (0) 20 7629 6602
Facsimile +44 (0) 20 7629 8876
www.phillips-auctions.com

Phillips
AUCTIONEERS

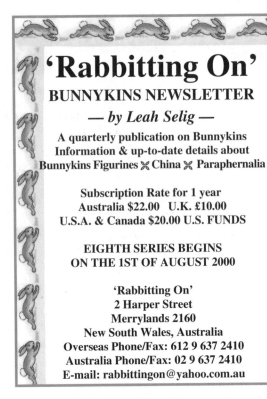
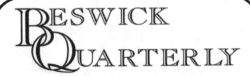